Introductory Musical Acoustics

Fourth Edition

Michael J. Wagner

 CONTEMPORARY PUBLISHING COMPANY OF RALEIGH, INC.

6001-101 Chapel Hill Road, Raleigh, NC 27607 • (919) 851-8221

www.contemporarypublishing.com

Publisher: Charles E. Grantham
Director of Marketing: Sherri Powell
Production Manager: Erika Kessler
Artwork: Pam Varney, Piedmont Litho
Printer: Edwards Brothers, Inc.
Cover Design: Contemporary Publishing Company of Raleigh, Inc.

ISBN: 0-89892-361-1

Table of Contents

Part I — Sound in Nature

Part III — Electronic Production and Reproduction of Sound: A Retrospective

Preface to the Fourth Edition

It's been more than 30 years since the original writing of this text. The world has seen many changes. Music's technology continues to evolve, or rather, to mature. Consider some symbols and words that held no meaning for anyone in 1976: PC, CD, word processing, Wi-Fi, DVD, MTV, MP3, cellular, digital, chip, bit, byte, meg, RAM, MIDI, Bluetooth, internet, twitter, quantize and even "analog," the term used to describe the acoustic process before digits took over. We could add to this list of "modern" or "contemporary" buzz words, yet chuckle at the terms left out or developed after this edition of the book was published. While Part I and parts of Part II of this text have held up quite well to the test of time, Part III, by its very nature, cannot. This edition amends and fills in the story of how our machines of music have continued to develop. Consider it a "history" of the pageant of music's technological changes.

The birth of three technologies since 1976 have profoundly transformed the way we humans think and live. First, consider the advent of the personal computer. On April Fool's Day, in 1976, Steve Wozniak and Steve Jobs released the Apple I computer and started Apple Computers. This began the personal compacting of knowledge and the organizing of it in ways that give us greater access to information, and the ability to act upon it…should we choose to do so. It has not provided us with more leisure time as was predicted, but rather, it has made us more efficient, shortening the time between "the need to know" and "knowing."

The personal computer has privatized our study, our word processing (we used to call this writing) and the storage of our personal data. The "computer," or "PC" as it is now called, processes information that used to take an entire office staff to accomplish. Our computers control other machines, sort astronomical quantities of numbers that represent things, and stores the processes for doing so in their programming. Therefore, we can do these "superhuman" tasks again and again. As expanded computer memory becomes available, we will undoubtedly design more and more complex tasks for our computers to perform for us…and at even greater speeds. Our lives will continue to change because of these processes. As I rewrite this "Preface" on my computer, my word processor corrects my spelling and suggests alternative words to me (if I ask) as I go. It automatically formats the text and offers many choices of fonts and colors. In 1975 the original version of this text was hand-written on yellow pads, then typed, clipped with scissors to reorganize content; then, of course, it was retyped again. This went on for four drafts, before it was finally typed on good paper stock so it could be photographed and typeset. As the prophetic Bob Dylan song purports, "Times, they are a-changin'."

The second "miracle technology" is the birth of the internet and its support network of an expanded global communications satellite system. The internet used to be referred to as the "information highway." Over time, it has become a gargantuan superhighway…maybe a better description might be, a colossal storage and delivery system.

Today, on a personal computer tied to the internet through a device called a modem, one can search virtually everywhere for information on nearly everything. Because batteries have improved so much and wireless technology has developed, one does not even need to plug-in any more. The internet and phone "cells" surround us. By accessing them through your PC, or your cell phone, you can see your house from satellite photos and find photographic maps of many places in the world. Real time videos of every conceivable nature abound. Present and future viewing of the weather anywhere in the world, is just a few key strokes away. You can watch, upload, or download photos or videos of anything conceivable. Shopping can be accomplished online and items are purchased using virtual credit transactions. Banking and investing are accomplished online. The computer has become a source of much of our entertainment. Through my computer and the internet, I look at and chat with my grandchildren who live five time-zones away, in England. Today, it seems almost absurd that there were recent times when none of this was possible. Arthur C. Clark, the late, visionary science fiction writer has stated that, "Any sufficiently advanced technology is indistinguishable from magic." It certainly seems so in the area of music technology.

The internet has even become the most popular place to begin research. In that regard, beginning with this 4th edition of this text, specific websites will be suggested to supplement the information contained within. When this "Preface" is finished to my satisfaction, it will have been sent via the internet…as will the entire book…to the publishers in Raleigh, NC at Contemporary Publishing Company. This "send" will happen nearly instantaneously. Today, more information is processed, quicker and more precisely than at any time in history. Our conceptual world has expanded exponentially.

The third of these new technologies is the invention of the "Walkman," the subsequent miniaturized MP3 player, and the cell phone. These are not trivial toys. Indeed, they may do for the music and entertainment industries what refrigeration has done for the food industry. There is now, for Everyman, a kind of "store it now and take it with you," and "throw it away when you're done," portable access to all kinds and styles of music…with incredibly good fidelity.

Listening (and learning) has become a private matter because these listening and learning machines are portable. They can go to school, to play, to work, to your yard, to the mountaintop, to primitive countries, and nearly everywhere. On the other hand, recorded music for many, has replaced silence, solitude, and reverie; and quite possibly, even contemplation, deep thought, and human information processing. Is this good? Time will tell. But the technologies are here. The Walkman technology has permeated our society. One worrisome note in this area is the way commercial music is paid for. There will be changes here in downloading and uploading, and we do not know how that will play out at this time.

None of these…the personal computer, the internet, or the Walkman were a part of our culture in 1976. In that year we celebrated the two hundredth birthday of our country, and marveled at the fidelity stored on "direct-to-disc," 33 and 1/3 rpm vinyl recordings; the very best recording technology available at that time. In those days of yesteryear, our telephones were tethered to the wall. As the vacuum tube gave way to the transistor, and the transistor gave way to the silicon chip and the microchip, they too have now given way to entire intricate micro-circuits. As technology moves forward, smaller and more complex electronic devices will do additional things faster and more efficiently. Some computers are now hand-held, married to cell phones, totally wireless, and battery driven. There is a momentum to our world's technology that seems to have its own motivation. Music's technological development has been, and will continue to be a part of that force. As musicians, educators and therapists, it is up to us to keep abreast of these developments.

Although the science of sound may legitimately be within the domain of the physicist, and many physicists are acousticians . . . and some, even amateur musicians…it is important to note that very few musicians are either physicists or acousticians. This does not indicate that musicians are not interested in acoustics or psychoacoustics. Indeed, many musicians and music educators lament a lack of clear knowledge in these areas, but feel that the language of acoustics, physics and mathematics is beyond their comprehension. The question that arises, is whether or not acoustics (including psychoacoustics) should be the concern of the physicist interested in acoustics, the physicist interested in music, the psychologist interested in psychology of music, teachers, music therapists or even the band "roadie!" and on and on. Who should be responsible for the passing on of our ever expanding acoustical knowledge?

Is it important that musicians be able to compute the wavelength of a clarinet's low "G" on a clarinet? Should a music educator be expected to calculate a music room's acoustic properties for an architect? Do musicians need to determine an orchestra's intensity level in dynes per square centimeter? Is the average pressure oscillation of a sound wavefront important to a musician? Should musicians be concerned with the Pythagorean comma, the diatonic comma, the syntonic comma, or the enharmonic diesis? The answer to all these questions is . . . probably not. While this information is interesting and enlightening to some, there are certainly important questions and answers about (1) acoustics, (2) how we hear, and (3) the electronic production and reproduction of sound that all musicians, music educators and music therapists ought to know in order to satisfactorily perform their jobs.

Where can musicians find this kind of acoustic information—important to their careers? For example, what are the "beats" heard when tuning? Should these beats be tuned out when tuning intervals other than the octave? Why doesn't a clarinet's register key produce an octave when opened, like other woodwinds? What exactly are the squeaks and squawks so often produced by student musicians? How can they be avoided? How do our ears work? Is deafness going to concern us or our students? How did our recording technology develop? How are electronic sounds produced and recorded?

It is the intent of this text to cover the broad areas of musical acoustics, how we hear (psychoacoustics), electronic sound recording, production, and reproduction…for musicians and music educators at a level commensurate with beginning study of the psychology of music. In this book, there are no formulas and their associated Greek symbols. There is little math and only basic explanations of physical laws and those associated with elementary electronics. This text is based upon the assumption that the term "INTRODUCTORY" means that no previous knowledge of the subject is necessary. The material covered in this text is not simple in a qualitative and quantitative sense; yet the subject matter is organized and sequenced so that it should be understandable to a musician reader who has only a high school general science background.

There is an inherent difficulty in organizing material for this kind of text. The problem is one of determining information that should be left out rather than what should be included. Some notable exclusions from this text are: a discussion of mass and force; photography of acoustical events; scientific and experimental instrumentation; relative harmonic strengths of familiar instrumental sounds; intensities of neurological signals; tracing of neurological pathways from the cochlea of the inner ear to the superior temporal gyrus of the brain; methods used for computation of frequencies for various temperament systems; technical specifications for electronic components; definitions and discussion of watts, amperes, and ohms; filtering and dithering of digital signals; the language of various binary coding systems; and … the list could go on and on.

The above information has been deliberately excluded from the text because the mere mention of these topics would require rather involved explanations that are simply not necessary for musicians in an introduction and general description of sound and its characteristics. An overview of what is included in this introductory text is placed at the beginning of each of the three main parts of this text.

A glossary giving definitions of important terms used in the text has been included on the page where the term is first introduced. Those words have been printed in **bold** in order to direct the reader's attention to the definitions placed in the side margin of the text. Terms which might be misinterpreted or may be ambiguous have "quotes" around them. Notes and references are superscripted[1] by chapter in the text, and may be found collected at the bottom of the page.

Each of the three main sections of this text has been introduced with suggested supplemental websites to visit for further or more detailed explanations. These websites have been chosen, not only for their information, but because of the stability of the organizations that have created them. Space has been allocated on each page for the jotting of notes and questions; a feature lacking in many texts. Footnotes and glossary terms are included on the page in which they are used. These are gifts of the publisher, Contemporary Publishing Company of Raleigh, North Carolina. For these and countless other reasons, you readers should be grateful to them.

Music and physics are really dynamic and have developed over the many years since Carl Seashore first published his *Psychology of Music*. Many older studies and the works of pioneering physicists ought to be read to fully comprehend acoustical principles. However, it would seem beneficial for musicians and neophyte acousticians to first become generally acquainted with INTRODUCTORY MUSICAL ACOUSTICS.

Enjoy the process.

Michael J. Wagner
Miami, Florida
2009

Foreword

In the many years that I have been teaching both undergraduate and graduate students in music education and music therapy courses, several thoughts have persisted. One question concerns why it is that only a few of my graduate students who became college teachers continue to teach courses in acoustics. It seems that very few developed that special "love" for acoustics and its subject matter that continues to excite only a limited number of us. Perhaps many of the "older" students first completed their academic work without first studying from an acoustics text specifically designed to spark their imagination and nurture that special excitement that stimulates a life-long "love affair" with its contents. Perhaps initial curiosity was drowned out by approaching the study of acoustics from a purely mathematical perspective as opposed to a more "musical" treatment. Perhaps therapy students could not relate to detailed acoustics study because they did not find reference to their specific populations or therapeutic concerns. A more parsimonious answer would probably attribute any lack of continued student interest to my ineffective teaching.

Regardless, I am most pleased to again provide a foreword, now to the fourth edition. I have used this book since it first appeared in manuscript. I use it because it was, and continues to be, written to excite, involve and engage the music student. It does not require previous knowledge (except the ability to think and to read) and it includes much information of interest to the music educator and the music therapist not found in other single texts. Because of its specific content and manner of presentation it is fun to use in the music classroom. While the word "fun" might seem peculiar in describing a textbook, anyone who knows this texts' author would concur that he would be most pleased if students could enjoy the study of acoustics. I am sure that sophisticated acousticians might questions some of its treatment, but it is not written for experts; students find it most accessible.

I hope that each student's initial reading of this text will develop into a more "romantic" interest leading to other, more detailed and comprehensive works. More importantly, I hope that every student who goes through these pages nurtures that child-like quality of questioning and wonderment while collecting exciting ideas to be thought about and even investigated in special projects. This is how some people develop an entire life's work—it often starts while reading a textbook, with a question that will just not go away.

Clifford K. Madsen, Ph.D.
Robert O. Lawton Distinguished Professor
Center for Music Research
School of Music
The Florida State University

Acknowledgements

The author wishes to gratefully thank those who read, critiqued, taught, explained, suggested and because of their knowledge and excitement, made this text come to life. There were two wonderful people who spent many on-task hours for and with me, editing and making suggestions for this edition of this text. They are:

Parts I & III—Richard Rose, D.M.A.
Dr. Richard F. Rose is a professor in the Commercial Music Department at Miami Dade College, Miami, Florida. Having received the Dr. Ruth Wolkowsky Greenfield Endowed Teaching Chair in Music in 2002, he was recently awarded the Sylvan E. Myers Endowed Teaching Chair. A sought-after instrumentalist, Dr. Rose continues to perform on electric and acoustic bass.

Part II—Vicki Wiman, M.S., CCC-A
Vicki Wiman has worked as an audiologist in a variety of settings over her career. Experiences include teaching at both University of Florida, The Florida State University, and a trainer for a digital hearing aid company. Clinical practice ranged from an ENT office, public schools, and currently Department of Veteran's Affairs and Office of Disability Determination.

And yet, there are more who have offered wise advice over the years; their time, energy, good wishes and excitement. Without these people too, the book would still be "in progress:" Erik Wagner, John Geringer, Amelia Main, Clement Pennington, Clifford Madsen, Harry Price and Randy DeWitt all come to mind when my thoughts turn to the creation of this book. Erika Kessler, my editor at Contemporary Publishing Company of Raleigh, North Carolina has been a delight to work with. But mostly, this time, my wife, Mary Ann Wagner gets the most credit for putting up with this retired author/curmudgeon. Thank you all.

About the Author

MICHAEL WAGNER,Ph.D., is a retired Professor and Director of Music Education and Fellow of the Florida International University Honors College, in Miami, Florida. He was a pioneering and distinguished member of the faculty at Florida International University during 31 of its first 32 years of existence. This award winning musician/teacher/researcher earned degrees from the State University of New York (SUNY) at Fredonia, Teachers College/Columbia University and a doctorate at The Florida State University, with further graduate work in music and performance at both the Eastman and Juilliard Schools of Music.

Before living in Florida, he was a member of the United States Military Academy Band at West Point, New York and later, a clarinet recitalist and concert performer. In the 1960s he taught in the public schools of New York State and later, was the college band and community orchestra director at the State University of New York (SUNY), Geneseo.

During the last few years of his teaching career, Dr. Wagner was an invited Fellow of the FIU Honors College. There, he taught a popular, yearlong course entitled, "Technology, the Leader of Humankind." His interests and rich experience have allowed him to combine the areas of music, music technology, and classroom management for educators in unique and interesting ways.

He is the author of two music education textbooks, many popular articles, and thirty-some research reports in the areas of music listening, teaching presentation style and teacher time use. He has also written, produced, and directed several video presentations for use in music classes. However, his students are certainly his best legacy. They dot the worldwide education landscape, and continue his legacy . . . leading and improving the ever-evolving process of Education.

His credentials include invitations to lecture about music and rehearsal technique, current technologies and classroom management in The Peoples' Republic of China, Australia, Germany, Great Britain, Sweden, and within the Caribbean basin, in the Republic of the Bahamas, Haiti, Puerto Rico, and Jamaica. In his consulting practice, he has helped educators improve their teaching technique throughout the United States as well.

As a former member of the US Army pistol team at West Point, and as a band director, Dr. Wagner is keenly aware of the hazards of too much sound. Over the period of his career, he has developed substantial hearing loss and tinnitus. He is somewhat evangelical about communicating how precious is our ability to hear and to comprehend our aural environment.

Part I

The first four chapters of this book are an introduction to certain physical laws governing sound, sources of sound and mediums through which sound most usually travels. Included are explanations of how acoustic music instruments produce sounds and their characteristic timbres. Also included are explanations of how our physical environment affects sound.

Here are some supplemental websites for you to visit for either another approach to the subject matter, or more detailed explanations.

Chapters 1, 2 and 4

http://en.wikipedia.org/wiki/Musical_acoustics

http://www.glenbrook.k12.il.us/GBSSCI/PHYS/CLASS/sound/soundtoc.html

http://numbera.com/musictheory/mechanics/physics.aspx

http://hyperphysics.phy-astr.gsu.edu/Hbase/sound/soucon.html

http://www.tufts.edu/as/wright_center/workshops/workshop_archives/physics_2003_wkshp/book/pom_book_acrobat_7.pdf

Chapter 3

http://hyperphysics.phy-astr.gsu.edu/HBASE/Music/musinscon.html

http://www.music.ed.ac.uk/euchmi/galpin/gxip.html

Sound In Its Simplest Form

CHAPTER 1

PHYSICAL VERSUS PSYCHOLOGICAL SOUND

Sound begins with physical **vibration**. To obtain an accurate picture of what is reported as "perceived" sounds or "psychological" sounds, an understanding of certain natural or physical components is necessary. What, in the environment, is necessary to produce sounds and for us to hear them?

There must first be some kind of energy and a source of vibration. In other words, something must be moved and consequently set into vibration. The energy of these vibrations then must be transmitted (travel) through some medium where they are received by either the ear or some form of recording device. Therefore, some kind of movement (energy), a vibrating source, a transmitting medium, and a receiver are needed in order for one to begin processing the incoming signals that are referred to as **sound**.[1]

"Sound" is a subjective term used by humans to report this aural psychological sensation. In an objective or physical sense, the phenomenon, of course, is vibration.[2] Remember the age-old question, "If a tree falls in a forest and no one is there to hear it, does the tree make a noise?" To a physicist (one who describes the physical laws of our universe), the answer is "yes!," because sound is vibration and surely the tree sets a great number of things into vibration as it falls. To a psychologist (one who investigates and describes the phenomena of the mind), if no one has had the sensation of hearing this tree fall, then, of course, it makes no sensation of sound or no noise. Who's right? It depends on one's point of view!

There are physical laws in the universe that act consistently and regularly. Each time a sound source is set into vibration it produces exactly the sound that universal physical laws allow it to produce. Musicians, especially, should be

---

[1] *Backus calls these three components source, medium and receptor.*
Backus, John, The Acoustical Foundations of Music; (New York: W. W. Norton & Company, Inc., 1969).

[2] *Sound, and hence music, can be analyzed in two ways: PHYSICALLY, by using instruments such as meters or other devices that display or record measurements of the properties of the sound, and PSYCHOLOGICALLY, by listening to the sound and attempting to ascertain its properties on the basis of our immediate experience.*
Howe, Hubert S., Jr., Electronic Music Synthesis; (New York: W.W. Norton & Company, Inc., 1975), p. 1.

VIBRATION: Any form of to-and-fro motion.

SOUND: A perceived, aural psychological sensation produced by vibration.

1

grateful for this. Imagine striking a bass drum and, instead of the resounding boom one would expect, the shriek of a wildcat or the sound of tires squealing sounded forth. Or worse, what if no sound at all was forthcoming? It is the consistency of these natural, predictable, physical laws that allows sounds and music to happen.

VIBRATION

An easy way to begin understanding the nature of vibration is to define the term. Vibration is any form of to-and-fro movement.[3] Visualize a string attached to a hook in the ceiling and a weight tied to the end of the string, thereby forming a pendulum. If the weight is set into motion by pulling it out of rest position (to the "to" end of the arc) and letting go, it will swing all the way to the "fro" end of the arc. The weight moves fastest when the string passes the point at which it is perpendicular to the floor (i.e., its former point of rest) and slows to a stop at the far end of the arc. Then it returns past the center to the other end of the arc (the "to" end again) where the whole sequence begins once more. The pendulum has been engaged in one kind of very slow vibration.

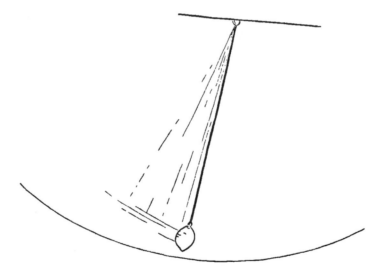

Figure 1-1

If that pendulum weight could trace a two-dimensional mark on a stationary piece of paper placed under it, the mark would be a straight line. However, if a moving roll of paper is passed slowly under the swinging pendulum and at right angles to the to-and-fro motion of the weight, the resultant mark would be a wavy line. This kind of wavy line is called a **sine wave**. It is a graph of the simplest and least complex kind of vibration that exists in time and

---

SINE WAVE: A graph of the simplest form of vibration showing motion in time and space.

[3] *Sometimes called oscillation, vibration is back and forth motion, one kind of oscillation. For further explanation, see:*
Jeans, Sir James; Science & Music; (New York: Dover Publications, Inc., 1968), pp. 28-32.

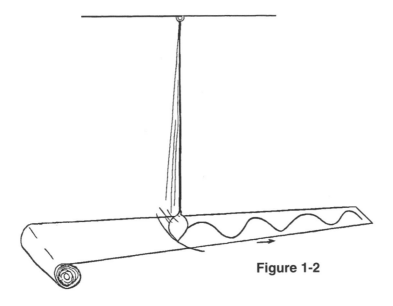

Figure 1-2

space[4]. The pendulum is traveling too slowly for humans to perceive this vibration as sound, of course, but if a machine were built that could generate this very basic kind of vibration rapidly and strongly enough, the result would be a "pure" tone (the result of simple vibration) called a **sine tone**. Such machines do indeed exist, and are called sine tone generators. Music **synthesizers** almost always have sine tone generators built into their architecture.

Simple Harmonic Motion

The pendulum-and-paper illustration is an example of **simple harmonic motion**. It is the simplest kind of vibration. Physical laws make the pendulum repeat its motion in equal intervals or periods of time, even though the distance traveled by the weight gets shorter and shorter. The pendulum's motion is therefore said to be periodic. It has completed one cycle or period when it has traveled through one "to" and one "fro" movement. If the time it takes for one cycle is (for instance) one second, the pendulum produces a sound of one cycle per second; or, said another way, the pendulum is vibrating at one hertz (Hz)[5].

Elasticity and Momentum

There are a number of natural laws governing the simple vibration of a pendulum and the formation of the sine wave upon the moving paper.[6] It is important to examine two of these. If the weight is pulled away from its perpendicular rest position and released, gravity will try to return it to its rest position.

---

[4] *Ibid., p. 28.*

[5] *The term "cycles per second" has been given the name Hertz (abbreviated Hz) in honor of the German physicist, Heinrich Hertz, who discovered the existence of radio waves.*

[6] *For a comprehensive discussion of physical quantities (i.e., length, time, velocity, force, mass, acceleration, pressure, work and power) fundamental to a more comprehensive study of vibration, see: Backus, op. cit., pp. 3-23.*

SINE TONE: The sound produced by sinusoidal vibration or oscillation.

SYNTHESIZER: An electronic music instrument that uses select tones, amplifiers and filters to create new musical sounds.

SIMPLE HARMONIC MOTION: Simple vibration. The motion takes place in a straight line and is periodic, i.e., the motion repeats itself in equal periods of time even though the distance traveled gets shorter and shorter. The motion is fastest as the body passes its center point of rest, and has moments at each extreme at which it is motionless. S.H.M. is perceived as a pure tone and results in a sine wave when graphed.

This natural tendency of a body to return to its rest position when deformed or displaced is called **elasticity**. However, the weight will not return to rest; instead it will overshoot its point of rest and proceed on. This tendency of the weight to overshoot its rest position is called **momentum**. Because of nature's laws of elasticity and momentum, when matter is set into vibration it takes time for it to settle back to its rest position. Some materials do not have very much elasticity and consequently do not vibrate very well. When a lump of wet clay is struck, it tends to stay in its new position. Because clay does not have much of a tendency to return to its original shape or position it may be said that it is not very elastic. Since vibration is due both to the elasticity and to the momentum of a material that has been set into motion, it can be readily observed that some substances will vibrate better than others.

Frequency and Amplitude

If a pendulum completes one complete cycle in the period of one second, it is said to have a **frequency** of one cycle per second (1 Hz). Frequency is the term used to describe the number of cycles (one "to" and one "fro" motion) per second at which a sound source is vibrating. Any sound source vibrates at the frequency at which its physical attributes most comfortably allow it to vibrate. In the case of the pendulum, the length of the string determines the frequency of its vibration. This particular frequency is called the natural or **resonant frequency** of a sound source. All materials (solids, liquids and gases) that have elasticity vibrate most easily at their resonant frequency. The resonant frequency of a sound source is a direct result of three factors: the material of which the object is made, whether it is under stress and its proportions. If the material vibrating is a stretched string fastened at both ends, as is the case with stringed instruments, the frequency obtained from setting it into vibration would be a direct result of the string's length and thickness, the tension on it, and the material of which the string is made.

The aural sensation that frequency causes is called **pitch**. Middle C, no matter what instrument produces it, vibrates 261.63[7] times per second. It may be said that the frequency of Middle C is 261.63 Hz, or that the pitch produced by a tone of 261.63 Hz is Middle C. One important feature of vibration is its rate (frequency). Subjectively speaking, humans call the result of the rate or speed of these vibrations, pitch.

Not only does the pendulum travel at a particular rate, it also travels through a certain distance that can be measured. This distance or the amount of displacement of a vibrating body is called **amplitude**. The psychological sensation caused by amplitude is **loudness**. The greater the amplitude (distance the vibrating body travels in its to-and-fro motion), the louder the sound will be. These subjective sensations occur only if the frequency and amplitude of the tone produced fall within the limits of hearing. Since so much of the study of sound depends upon the perceptual limits of our hearing mechanism, it would be wise to look briefly at the ranges of most human aural perception.

---

[7] *The United States Standards Association, the Acoustical Society of America and the National Bureau of Standards have agreed to 440 Hz as the frequency rate of Concert A. Therefore, in equal temperament, Middle C has a frequency of 261.63 Hz.*

ELASTICITY: The tendency of a displaced body to return to its point of rest.

MOMENTUM: The tendency of a displaced body to overshoot its point of rest.

FREQUENCY: The number of cycles (complete vibrations) which take place in a fixed period of time. An acoustical definition of frequency is the number of sound waves passing a given point in one second.

RESONANT FREQUENCY: The frequency at which a body tends to vibrate due to its natural characteristics of size, shape, molecular composition, and the stress the body is under.

PITCH: Our perception of frequency. The greater the frequency, the higher the perceived pitch.

AMPLITUDE: The distance through which a vibrating body moves. That is, the amount of displacement of a vibrating body.

LOUDNESS: Our perception of amplitude. The greater the amplitude, the louder the perceived sound. This is tempered somewhat by the fact that we do not hear equally well at all frequencies.

Perception and Measurement of Frequency

Generally, humans perceive sounds or vibrations no lower than 20 Hz and no higher than 20,000 Hz.[8] For comparison, the lowest note (A) on a piano has a frequency of 27.5 Hz. It causes vibrations that occur 27.5 times per second. The highest note (C) has a frequency of 4186 Hz or 4186 vibrations a second. Tones below 20 Hz and above 20,000 Hz are a great deal like the "tree in the forest" since they exist as vibration, but cannot be perceived by most listeners. There are some people who can perceive frequencies a little lower, and some who can perceive frequencies a little higher. However, as people get older, the upper frequency limit of the audible range becomes lower, due to a general degeneration of the hearing mechanism and sometimes due to hearing damage caused by external or environmental events such as exposure to loud noises. Sometimes there are also selective hearing losses in the middle of the frequency spectrum. An inability to perceive certain frequencies and amplitudes normally within audible limits is termed a **hearing loss**.[9] After age 50, it is not uncommon to perceive sounds no higher than about 10,000 Hz.

One way of measuring the frequency of a tone is to compare it to a reference frequency. When musicians tune with each other they do just that. For more precise measurements, machines have been developed to help make more accurate judgments. An early-model "tuner" is a disc with alternating light-and-dark squares that rotates at a set speed for a given frequency. As a tone is played into a microphone, a neon bulb flashes at the tone's exact frequency. If the dark squares of the disc pass the light at the same frequency with which the light flashes on, the dark squares seem to remain motionless. This machine utilizes a stroboscope to produce the blinking light and is known as a stroboscopic tuner, or "strobe" tuner. It uses the stroboscopic effect to measure the frequency of vibration.[10] If the dark squares seem to move slowly in one direction or the other, the tone is slightly flatter (lower) or sharper (higher) than the reference frequency.[11] Today, with man's ability to miniaturize electronics, "tuners" use the circuitry of the microchip to achieve the same end. These devices are extremely accurate and measurements as fine as one one-hundredth of a semi-tone are possible. For the sake of more precise measurement the name **cent** (1/100 of a semi-tone) is used to describe the amount of pitch deviation. This seems to be a more convenient description for musicians than the number of Hz that a pitch deviates from some reference standard. To illustrate, if a 27.5 Hz tone (low A) is sharp by one vibration per second,

---

[8] *Department of Veterans Affairs staff at Mountain Home, TN, Long Beach, CA, Nashville, TN. The Audiology Primer for Students and Health Care Professionals, 3rd Ed. Retrieved May 2009, from http://etsu.edu/crhs/commdis/audiology/audiologyebook.aspx.*

[9] *Ibid., p. 83.*

[10] *There are a number of other illustrations of the stroboscopic effect. Automobile engines are adjusted by using a flashing light pointed at a mark on the engine's timing wheel. Wagon wheels in movies of the old west seem to be moving backward or forward and often too slowly depending on the speed of the film's frames passing the camera's lens (24 fps) and the actual speed of the spokes of the wheel.*

[11] *Stroboconn Operation and Service Manual, for model 6T-5; Conn Corporation; 616 Enterprise Drive; Oak Brook, Illinois, 60521; p. 6.*

> **HEARING LOSS:** The inability to perceive certain frequencies and amplitudes which are within the common limits of perception.
>
> **CENT:** One hundredth of a chromatic semitone. It is the unit most commonly used to represent pitch deviation.

the error is approximately 1/27 of the frequency. A 4,000 Hz tone, sharp by one vibration, has an error of only 1/4000 of the frequency. For most kinds of pitch measurement it seems easier to divide each semi-tone into one hundred parts that are equal, no matter what the frequency, and use the number of cents sharp or flat to describe fluctuations or deviations in pitch or frequency.

Perception and Measurement of Amplitude

Some sounds are too soft to be audible and others so loud that they are painful and can actually cause damage to our ears. The perception of amplitude is dependent not only upon the sensitivity and limits of hearing, but also upon the frequency of sound. Low frequencies require more power or energy to be heard than do high frequencies. Therefore, what is perceived as a soft low A on the piano (27.5 Hz) must have a much greater amplitude than Middle C (261.63 Hz) for the two tones to be judged equally loud. Loudness level has been computed by determining an average "threshold of audibility."[12] Scientists have determined this threshold of audibility by taking the frequency of 1000 Hz and decreasing its amplitude to the point at which it can no longer be perceived by people with "normal" hearing. This zero loudness level is an arbitrary point of reference for comparing the intensities of tones of different loudness. As can be seen in Figure 1-3, the sensitivity of hearing varies with the frequency of the tone being produced.

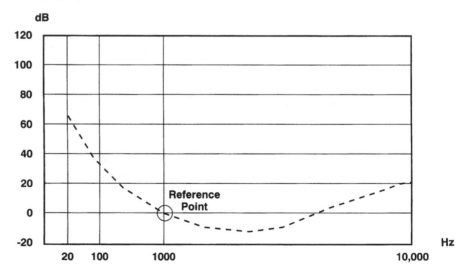

Figure 1-3. Minimum perception of tonal intensity from 20 Hz through 10,000 Hz. This curve is based on the work of Fletcher and Munson at Bell labs (1933), It was made by asking people to judge when pure tones of two different frequencies were the same loudness. This is a very difficult judgment to make, and the curve is the average result from many subjects, so it should be considered a general indicator rather than a prescription as to what a single individual might hear.

- - - - - - - - - indicates threshold of audibility (after Fletcher and Munsen).

---

[12] *The Fletcher/Munsen curve is important because speaker calibration does not take our non-linear hearing into account.*

The intensity (or energy) of sound (a product of amplitude) is usually measured in **decibels**.[13] Because it takes ten times the energy or intensity to produce a tone that is perceived as twice as loud, it is easier to think in terms of decibels (abbreviated dB) than to think of intensity level. For example, a tone of 10 dB is 10 times the intensity of 0 dB (the reference threshold of audibility), a tone of 20 dB is 100 times the intensity of 0 dB, a 30 dB tone is 1000 times the intensity, and so on, until 90 dB (still fairly comfortable to listen to) is 1,000,000,000 (1 billion) times the intensity of the threshold of audibility. Decibels are measured using a sound level meter. The meter contains a microphone, and the sound energy impinging upon the microphone's diaphragm (SPL or Sound Pressure Level) is displayed on a readout in decibels. In this way a level of sound intensity can be obtained. To illustrate how sound intensity or amplitude relates to frequency: the low A (27.5 Hz) on the piano will take approximately 64 dB for one to minimally perceive it. Stated another way, low A at 64 dB is at the threshold of audibility; Middle C (261.63 Hz) requires about 20 dB to be minimally perceived; the C two octaves above Middle C (1046.5 Hz) is perceived at approximately 0 dB; and the highest note on the piano (4186 Hz) is detected at about -17 dB. This is self-explanatory in Figure 1-3. These differences in intensity levels for various pitches are due to the fact that our hearing apparatus does not respond equally to tones of different pitches.

At the other end of the amplitude spectrum, one does not stop hearing when sounds get too loud. Instead, when the sound intensity becomes great enough, pain is experienced. The commonly accepted pain threshold occurs at approximately 120 dB.[14] That is, most people experience pain when subjected to sounds of this intensity. Obviously, this too depends upon frequency. Permanent damage to hearing can result if one persists in repeated and prolonged exposure to very loud sounds. A discussion of kinds and causes of hearing loss is presented in Chapter 6.

The measuring of amplitude and its related subjective loudness can actually be quite a complex process. Consider an orchestral piece that contains an unaccompanied low C (32.7 Hz) for pipe organ that is marked in the score as pianissimo.[15] If one measures the dB level of this tone as it is played, it could quite possibly have an intensity equal to the full orchestra playing forte without the pipe organ (Remember, low Hz and high Hz require more power to be heard.). Because loudness is subjectively perceived, the amplitude or intensity measurements may sometimes seem in conflict with what we perceive. Is the physical sound more important than the perception of the sound, or is the reverse true?

---

[13] *The basic unit of intensity is the bel, named after Alexander Graham Bell. Since more precise measurements are required, the power or intensity of a sound is measured in units equal to 1/10 of a bel or decibels (dB - abbreviation). One decibel is approximately the smallest change in intensity that the human ear can detect.*

[14] *Barthlomew, Wilmer T., Acoustics of Music (Englewood Cliffs, New Jersey: Prentice-Hall, Inc., 1964), p. 211.*

[15] *Camille Saint Saëns' 3rd "Organ" Symphony, 2nd Movement*

DECIBEL: A unit of sound intensity. The expression of intensity in dB (abbreviation) is a relationship between the sound being measured and a reference intensity upon which the sound level meter is calibrated.

THE TRANSMISSION OF SOUND

Until now, our discussion has been concerned mainly with parameters of the vibrating body itself, and briefly with the human hearing apparatus as a receiver of sounds. Sound in nature must travel through various media (solids, liquids, gases) to get from its origin to the hearing apparatus. Usually, though not always, this **transmitting medium** is the atmosphere. If you are sitting near a table or desk, put one ear firmly upon the surface and listen. Sounds are constantly being transmitted through many objects (media). You will no longer hear those sounds when you remove your ear. This is because these sounds lack sufficient amplitude to set the surrounding air in enough motion to make the vibrations travel to your ear at an intensity greater than the threshold of audibility. Sound energy dissipates more quickly in the air than it does in most solid media.

Media

Solids and liquids are, in many cases, better transmitting media than air because, although they are more dense, they have an elastic quality. Sound travels great distances in water and in steel. Folklore states that in the early days of our country, Native Americans in the "old West" would put an ear to a railroad track or to the ground to hear if a train or a horseback rider was coming. They would do so because the sound of the train's wheels against the steel track or hoof beats on the hard ground would arrive much faster and from much further away than would the same sounds traveling through the air.

Just how is sound transmitted? All matter is made up of molecules and sound is carried by the to-and-fro movement of these molecules. If a bass drum head is struck, the molecules of the drum head have been moved, as well as those of the air on either side of the head. The disturbed molecules of air move

TRANSMITTING MEDIA: A transmitter of vibration from a sound source to a receiver (the ear or a microphone). Mediums must also be elastic in order for vibration to take place.

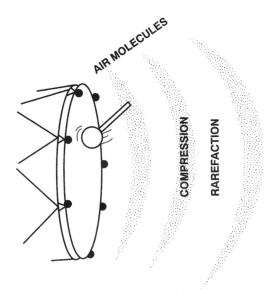

Figure 1-4. Compression waves traveling away from bass drum head.

past their point of rest and, in effect, compress against each other. That point where these molecules compress or compact is called a **compression**. Then, as the molecules move back toward their points of rest and overshoot their marks, a **rarefaction** occurs. This is a very small partial vacuum created in the air due to the molecules of air having moved away from that point. Explained by the laws of elasticity and momentum, molecules of the transmitting medium begin to vibrate.[16] As they move, they bump other molecules and a wave of disturbance begins moving away from the sound source in an ever-widening wave of compressions and rarefactions. These waves, traveling through the transmitting medium, are analogous to the action of the sound source. If the sound source is an elastic medium, it will settle to rest slowly (as in the case of the pendulum). Each time it travels through one cycle, it disturbs the transmitting medium that is set in motion at the same frequency and amplitude as the sound source. These compression waves travel until they bump into another medium. One of the things they may bump into is the ear. That's not all, however. These compressional wavefronts bump into walls, chairs, and other hard surfaces where they, by **reflection**, travel back again away from whatever they bump. Listeners hear these reflected sound waves and perceive them as part of the total sound. Reflected sound waves are called **echoes**. These waves can travel back through each other, yet do not disturb the frequency, amplitude or shape of other compressional wavefronts through which they pass.[17] As these sound waves travel back and forth, they become weaker and weaker. Their energy dissipates as the sound waves travel outward through space.

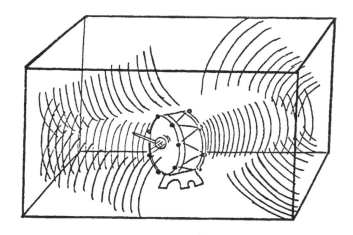

Figure 1-5. Sound reflection (echoes) inside a room.

---

[16] *For a more comprehensive treatment of how sound travels see:*
   Olsen, Harry F., Musical Engineering; (New York: McGraw-Hill Book Company, Inc., 1952), pp. 4-7.

[17] *Another of the physical "miracles" for which we can be very grateful is that soundwaves do not lose their characteristics when they meet and travel through other sound waves. Imagine, if these waves did not retain their identities, what two people talking together might sound like. Hearing an orchestra playing together, for instance, would be physically impossible.*

COMPRESSION: A point in space where a number of molecules which have been set into motion in effect bunch up causing an unusual number of molecules to occupy the same space.

RAREFACTION: A point at which the usual number of molecules which occupy a given space are temporarily out of position, causing a partial vacuum to occur.

REFLECTION: The bouncing back of sound waves as they strike a surface more dense than that in which they are traveling.

ECHOES: Sound waves which have been reflected.

If, instead of hitting a hard surface, soundwaves hit a curtain or a block of acoustic tile (made of pressed fibers), random dissipation and reflection take place very rapidly within the fibers of the material. In effect, the sound waves become trapped. The many tiny surfaces of the soft material reflect the sound waves in and out of the many chambers created by the material's fibers. Within these fibers, sound energy is quickly dissipated, and very little energy is reflected back. Therefore, the sound is said to have been absorbed; although in reality it is rampant reflection that actually occurs.

In air, sound waves, travel away from their source at about 1130 feet or 344 meters per second.[18] Expressed another way, it will take sound approximately 4.7 seconds to travel one mile through air. The air temperature, wind factors, and barometric pressure tend to change these figures slightly; but for our purposes, sound may be thought of as traveling through the earth's atmosphere at approximately 1130 feet per second.

Remember that it is not the molecules of the transmitting medium that travel out from the sound source but rather the energy that is transmitted by the sound source being set into vibration. Each molecule moves in its own sphere of elasticity, bumps others and returns. As energy dissipates, amplitude decreases, and the molecules return to their rest position. This principle can be illustrated by visualizing styrofoam pellets floating on and covering the surface of a pan of water. A marble dropped into the center of the pan when the water is still will force the individual pellets to move up, down, and sideways, but no individual pellet moves away from the point of disturbance to the sides of the pan and back. Only the energy of the disturbance is transmitted from the source of vibration to the side of the pan and back. The pellets may be thought of as molecules of a transmitting medium. Remember however, this is a two-dimensional illustration. When sound travels, it travels spherically in three dimensions outward from the source of the disturbance.

Resonance

Another interesting facet of sound vibration is that bodies other than a particular sound source have natural or resonant frequencies. It is well known that many people sing in the shower. This is probably because bathrooms are constructed of mostly hard surfaces and will reflect sound waves back to the singer. The echoes caused by bathroom singing seem very pleasant. One may notice, however, that there are one or more frequencies (pitches) that echo louder or stronger than all the rest. This extra loud **resonance** is the excitation of another body that "likes" to vibrate or has a naturally resonant frequency at a particular pitch. The composition of that body is particularly sensitive to vibrations of that frequency. Now instead of this surface simply reflecting the compressional

RESONANCE: The transmission of vibration from (sympathetic vibration) one body to another (usually through air). The frequency of the first body must be exactly or very nearly the natural frequency of the second body.

[18] *Actually, the speed of sound at 68° F. (20° C.) is 1130 feet (344 meters) per second; at 32° F. (0° C.), its speed is 1087 feet (331.5 meters) per second. For some practical purposes, the speed of sound may be represented as 1100 feet per second, which is about 13 miles per minute or 768 miles per hour. Backus, op. cit., p. 44.*

wavefront, the body itself begins vibrating at that frequency and transmits its vibrations as well as the already present frequency of the sound source, thus reinforcing that sound. Energy is not created by resonance; but resonant bodies use sound energy more efficiently at particular frequencies.

The excitation of a second sound source is sometimes called sympathetic vibration. These resonant frequencies are regarded as very bad in the building of concert halls. The reasons are obvious. Architects make many acoustical tests to ensure that no particular frequency will be reinforced more so than all other frequencies during a performance in that hall.[19]

There are cases where it is desirable to resonate or reinforce as many pitches as possible. The sounding board of a piano, the large wooden surface placed near the strings, is made of special wood and is slightly arched to amplify and resonate the piano's relatively weak string tones. This is also the case with all string instruments. The beautiful wooden box under the strings of a guitar, violin, or other stringed instrument is its resonator. A string instrument's value exists in the resonator's ability to produce tones that are not widely disparate in amplitude.

The principles of simple harmonic motion and how sound is transmitted have been discussed in this chapter. Two parameters of sound, frequency and amplitude, have been explained, as well as how pure sounds are transmitted from their source to a listener. In the next chapter another parameter of sound not found in simple harmonic motion will be discussed, the parameter of timbre or tone quality.

DISCUSSION QUESTIONS FOR CHAPTER ONE

1. How might a physicist describe music?

2. How might a psychologist describe music?

3. Is sound a physical or psychological phenomenon? Explain.

4. Describe how the time interval between when a flash of lightning is seen and when the thunder is heard can be used to estimate the distance of an electrical storm from the listener.

---

[19] *The same principle is responsible for the fact that troops are ordered to break cadence when crossing a bridge, so as to prevent vibration and possible breaking of the bridge if its natural frequency happens to coincide with that of the regular tread of marching.*
Bartholomew, op. cit., p. 28.

5. Listen to a recording of a low organ tone (e.g. Saint-Saëns' Third Symphony, second movement). Is the organ tone subjectively loud? Objectively loud?

6. Find a resonant frequency in your bathroom. What is its pitch? Is there more than one resonant frequency? Which body created the resonant frequency? What are its dimensions and characteristics?

Complex Sound
CHAPTER 2

QUALITY AND TIMBRE

Various names have been given to the parameter of sound that distinguishes one tone from another. Even though two tones may have the same frequency and amplitude (pitch and loudness) they may sound different from each other. Some call this difference **timbre**; others call it tone color, and still others, quality. Various sound sources produce kinds of vibrations that are alike in frequency and amplitude yet sound dissimilar. Even human voices are unlike each other. In this chapter, the reasons for those differences between sound sources that produce characteristic qualities or timbres will be explored.

People learn to recognize one quality of tone from another very early in life. A young baby is able to distinguish its mother's voice from all other adult female voices in the first few months of life and very possibly prior to birth, in the womb. A baby will respond to its mother's voice even in a room full of people. Differences between adult male and female voices are also discerned very early. In the first year of life, a baby reacts discriminately to different environmental sound sources and easily discriminates between the sounds associated with preparing a bottle of formula and other kitchen sounds. Adults make many finer timbre discriminations. Many recognize the sound of their own car's engine from all others. Most musicians can even discern one orchestral voice from all others when listening to a full orchestra. It would seem that these subtle differences in tone quality are perceived early and easily by our marvelous hearing apparatus, though all the physiological reasons for our perception of these quality differences are not yet fully understood.[1]

HARMONICS

In the last chapter we learned that a "pure" or simple tone results from a sine wave, and that these tones are sometimes referred to as sine tones. Each

TIMBRE (Tone Color, Quality): A sensory characteristic determined mainly by the degree of complexity of the vibration of a body. Many subjective terms have arisen to describe the differences in vibrating complexity (richness, brightness, full, brilliant, dark, etc.). Research has failed to find acoustical consistencies of timbre which match such subjective descriptions.

---

[1] *Seashore added one further musical descriptor of timbre: time. In fact, he and his Psychology of Music laboratory staff coined the term "sonance" to describe the effect of timbre through time. As early as 1926, Metfessel described effects of duration on timbre. See:*
Metfessel, Milton, Techniques for Objective Study of the Vocal Art; *University of Iowa Studies in Psychology, (Iowa City, Iowa: University Press, IX, 1926), pp. 1- 40.*
Seashore, Carl E., Psychology of Music; *(New York: McGraw-Hill Book Company, Inc., 1938), pp. 103-124.*

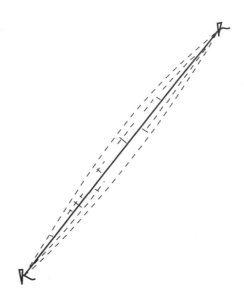

Figure 2-1. A stretched string producing its fundamental frequency.

sine tone is said to have only one frequency. This frequency might more properly be referred to as a **fundamental frequency** because it is not the only tone present in most sounds. Most sounds in the environment are not pure tones, but are composites of simultaneous sounds called **overtones**, **harmonics**, or **partials**.[2] When a stretched string is set into vibration, the whole string vibrates. The fundamental frequency of the tone produced is determined by the length, thickness, tension, and material composition of the string. It is the vibration of the whole length of the string that determines the pitch we perceive it to play. Yet it is important to note that as the whole length of the stretched string moves in its fundamental to-and-fro motion, the string is also set into vibration in fractional parts. That is, each half of the string vibrates (See Figure 2-2) in its own to-and-fro motion even as it vibrates as a whole. This harmonic vibration is a completely natural phenomenon resulting in what is called the first overtone.

Overtones are frequencies above the fundamental frequency that are the result of the complex vibration of the sound source. To further describe these harmonic vibrations, not only does a body vibrate in halves, but also in thirds, quarters, fifths, sixths, etc. The frequency of each of these tones is higher than the fundamental. Also each of these frequencies can be represented by a whole-

FUNDAMENTAL FREQUENCY: The frequency at which the sound source vibrates as a whole. This may also be expressed as the lowest pitch that the sound source is capable of producing.

OVERTONE: One of the frequencies produced by the complex vibration of a body. Any overtone will be higher than the fundamental frequency and a whole-number multiple of it. The fundamental is not an overtone.

HARMONICS (Harmonic Series): A series of tones (overtones) caused by the complex vibration of a body. Each harmonic has a frequency which is a whole number of times the frequency of the fundamental. The fundamental frequency may also be referred to as the first harmonic.

PARTIAL: Any component of the harmonic series including the fundamental. Often the terms overtone, harmonic and partial are used interchangeably, although purists would argue that they should not be.

---

[2] *For a very interesting treatise on the "Composition of Vibrations," the reader is directed to the Alexander J. Ellis English translation of Hermann L.F. Helmholtz's* On the Sensations of Tone as a Basis for the Theory of Music; *from the 1885 edition.*
Helmholtz, Hermann L.F., On the Sensations of Tone, *fourth edition, trans. Alexander J. Ellis, (New York: Dover Publications, Inc., 1954), pp. 25-36.*
FURTHER READING:
Bartholomew, Wilmer T., Acoustics of Music, *(Englewood Cliffs, New Jersey: Prentice-Hall, Inc., 1964), pp. 7-11.*
Culver, Charles A., Musical Acoustics, *(New York: McGraw-Hill Book Company, 1969), pp. 102-108.*

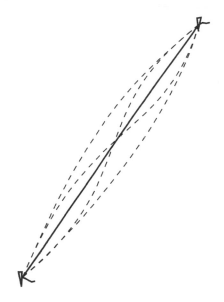

Figure 2-2. A stretched string producing its fundamental frequency and the first overtone (one octave above the fundamental).

number multiple of the fundamental frequency. Theoretically, the harmonic series continues upward through the sound spectrum much higher than the limits of human audibility.

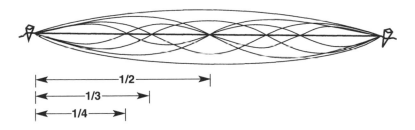

Figure 2-3. Complex vibration of a stretched string.

Harmonic Relationships to Pitch and Frequency

Since complex vibrations result in the simultaneous production of other higher pitches, the vibrating string example will illustrate this point. If a violin produces its lowest note, the G below Middle C, it produces a fundamental frequency of 196 Hz. If the string is also vibrating in halves, each half will produce a frequency of 392 Hz or one octave above the fundamental. The whole-number multiple in this case is 2. Since the string also vibrates in three equal segments (196 Hz x 3), it also produces a tone of 588 Hz. This tone is the D above the first overtone or an octave and a fifth above the fundamental. To go one step further, four equal segments produce a frequency of 784 Hz that is two octaves above the fundamental. An illustration of an overtone series starting on C (65.41 Hz) two octaves below Middle C through the fifteenth overtone has been constructed in

Figure 2-4. It can be readily seen that the complex vibration of a body results in not one, but a theoretically infinite number, of tones above the fundamental. With the exception of octaves, none of the overtones is exactly in tune with tones of our modern tuning system. Beginning with the sixth overtone, these frequency differences become particularly noticeable when compared to tones of a diatonic scale.

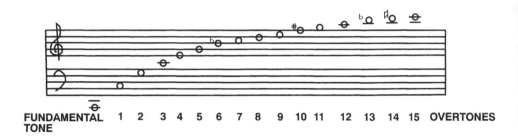

FUNDAMENTAL TONE   1   2   3   4   5   6   7   8   9   10   11   12   13   14   15   OVERTONES

Figure 2-4. An Overtone series based upon the fundamental C, two octaves below Middle C.

Harmonic Relationships to Loudness and Amplitude

The tones of the overtone series resulting from the complex vibration of a sound source are not all produced in equal strength. If they were, all musical tones would sound equally rich or, at least, alike. It seems that the relative intensity of each overtone to its particular fundamental plays a part in determining the timbre of a particular sound. In fact, there seem to be at least two different phenomena that help determine the overtone content of a given sound. The first, as has been stated, is the fact that each musical instrument produces complex vibrations, or vibrations that contain overtones. Certain of these are more prominent (have more amplitude) than others. This difference in prominence plays a very important role in determining a sound's timbre. If we could assume, when analyzing sounds for their overtone content, that because one tone had a strong first overtone then all tones produced by that instrument would have strong first overtones, harmonic analysis would be a relatively easy operation. In that case, when the harmonic complexities for one tone of an instrument had been determined, the harmonic complexities for each subsequent tone could be assumed. Fortunately, this is not the case, for if this were true, the many varieties of timbre or tone color produced by musical instruments would not be possible.

This brings us to the second phenomenon of harmonic analysis: **formants.**[3] Each instrument has certain frequencies that are more resonant than others, called

3 Bolt, R.H., "Wanted—The Formant," Journal of the Acoustical Society of America, XX (1948), p. 66.

Roederer, Juan G., Introduction to the Physics & Psychophysics of Music, (London: The English Universities Press, Ltd., 1974), p. 109.

> **FORMANT: A broad resonance region that enhances the upper harmonics lying in a fixed frequency range.**

formants. When an overtone falls within or near a formant area, it is strengthened. It is these formant areas in each instrument that help determine the timbre of its tones. Formants are fairly broad bands of resonance that strengthen the overtones falling within those frequency ranges.

It is the combination of complex vibrations and formants that gives instruments (and the human voice) their characteristic qualities. Some sounds have very weak fundamentals yet, with a strongly reinforced harmonic series, the tone becomes very different and often quite pleasing to hear. An excellent example of this phenomenon involves our own voice. Vocal folds (vocal cords) that have been removed from human cadavers but left in the trachea (windpipe) have been artificially excited by introducing air from below. When stimulated in this way, vocal folds produce sounds much like a "Bronx cheer" or "lip fart." One would call this sound at best "unnatural." It is the shape of the mouth and the many unique resonating chambers in the head that produce the vocal timbre one has come to expect from a human voice. The complexities of these resonating chambers allow one to change their vocal timbre within a wide range of natural limits.

Remember, many instruments (especially stringed instruments) depend upon the body of the instrument for reinforcement of the fundamental and its overtones. The timbre of most musical tones is changed by the shape and size of the resonator. These resonators did not come by their shapes accidentally. Instrument makers are constantly experimenting to find shapes, sizes, and materials that will reinforce particular overtones and in turn enrich the tone quality of musical instruments. What would happen if certain overtones were weakened or simply not present in familiar complex sounds? If you've ever listened to an old 78 rpm record, you may have noticed that the sound reproduction did not seem natural. It may have sounded as if you were listening to the performance through a keyhole or far away and through very heavy curtains. These "dull" timbres occur because the upper overtones are weak or missing entirely. The recording industry of today, as will be seen in Part III of this book, pays particular attention to the number and relative strength of overtones as they are recorded, in order that the most realistic possible sound is reproduced.[4]

---

[4] *Nimbus Recording Company has released a set of CDs (compact discs) that are recordings of old 78 rpm records. The lengths to which the company went were extraordinary. They found the best existing 78 rpm record player available, new Scotch thistle phono needles, and rented a remote farm house in the English countryside, where they set up the most sophisticated, contemporary one-microphone recording setup possible. Then, in the dead of night, for the quietest recording possible, they played virgin 78 rpm records into the new recording equipment; all to get an idea of what fidelity was possible on the playback equipment of the 1920s. The results must be heard to be believed. There is more "recording" on old records than most phonographs of the time could reproduce.*
But even with these extraordinary techniques, the recordings "sound like" 78 rpm records. They have a distinct set of timbres! Nimbus Records, Great Singers, 1909 - 1938, "Prima Voce".
NI 7801, 1989., for instance. There are quite a few available.

ENVELOPE

Music researchers have noted that when the initial attack is clipped from tape recordings of sustained instrumental and vocal sounds, their tonal identities are much more difficult to ascertain.[5] To identify sounds listeners depend upon other characteristics of sound than the relative strengths and weaknesses of the harmonic components of those sounds. The attack and release of a tone are also used as clues as to a sound's identity. If one thinks of a tone as it exists through time, the beginning, middle, and end of a tone each have characteristics of their own. This temporal shape of a tone is called its **envelope**.

Temporal Factors

With the invention and fairly widespread circulation of electronic musical instruments, musicians have noted that in order to duplicate the sounds of more traditional instruments, they have to synthesize four different parts of a tone's duration or shape as it exists in time. The first sound to be heard is called the initial attack. There follows an initial decay or softening of the sound that is still perceived as part of the attack. The sustained portion of the tone follows, and the

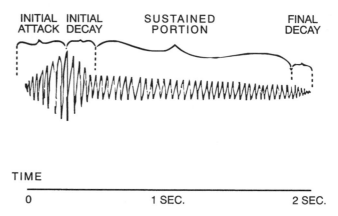

Figure 2-5. The envelope of a musical tone played at mm=60 for two beats.

tone concludes with a final release or decay.[6] Makers of electronic musical instruments, when designing and building them, must take both harmonic content and envelope into consideration. Synthesists, in order to create or modify sounds, manipulate a control parameter labeled "ADSR." Those letters correspond to "A" attack, "D" initial decay, "S" sustain, and "R" release. Imagine the many kinds of sound possible, using the relative strengths and weaknesses of the overtones of a harmonic series combined with the possible temporal designs of the four parts of a tone's envelope. It would seem that, since the beginning of

---

ENVELOPE: The temporal shape of a tone consisting of an attack (or onset), initial decay, sustain, and release or final decay.

[5] Elliot, Charles A., "Attacks & Releases as Factors in Instrument Identification," Journal of Research in Music Education, Vol. 23, No.1, Spring, 1975), pp. 35-40.

[6] Howe, Hubert S., Jr., Electronic Music Synthesis, (New York: W. W. Norton & Company, Inc., 1975), p. 8.

time, when man needed a particular sound for his music, he took what was available or built a new instrument. Today, with the electronic synthesizer, there are at one's fingertips, the possibilities for many new sounds.

Description of Sound

As a sound is perceived, certain subjective judgements can be made about it. It may be said, concerning its frequency, that the sound is relatively high or low. If more precision is necessary, it may be noted that the pitch is close to Middle C. When describing amplitude, it could be stated that a sound is loud or soft, or that one sound is louder than another sound. To be even more exacting, it can be ascertained that a sound has an intensity of 50 dB. Concerning quality or timbre, we could describe the sound as "flutelike," "buzzy," "bright," or use other general descriptors, often in foreign languages. Musicians are generally not very exact about descriptions of sounds unless they can relate the sound heard to another model of that sound, and compare the two. More objectively, all sounds have four parameters: frequency, amplitude, timbre, and envelope. By determining the specific characteristics of each of these parameters of a tone, it is possible (within the limits of present technology) to describe that tone quite precisely. Therefore, a very close approximation of most musical sounds may be reconstructed, although it is the human inexactitudes that keep "perfect" electronic sounds from sounding really "realistic."

NOISE

The envelopes of most tones begin with non-musical elements. These percussive beginnings of tones occur at the attack and initial decay segments of the envelope and are in actuality, more **noise** than they are music. Noise is generally considered to be aperiodic vibration that contains **inharmonic overtones**. This is a two-fold definition. Aperiodic vibration is to-and-fro motion that does not have regular frequency. If the pendulum described in Chapter 1 were forced to vibrate in a manner that did not allow equal swinging on both sides of the point of rest, or if each swing were at a different speed, noise would be the result. The period of the swing would vary with each cycle. Obviously, no fixed pitch could result from this random periodicity. The sensation caused by sound sources that are forced into this aperiodic vibration is described as noise. That is, sounds of no fixed pitch. Inharmonic overtones, the second part of the definition, are a product of sound sources that have inconsistencies of tension, stress and configuration. Such sources, when vibrating, do not displace as wholes, halves, thirds, etc., but rather displace in a complex, random, and aperiodic fashion. The resultant sound is described as noise.

Musical Uses of Noise

Noise is not a thing apart from those tones that are called musical, and some noises are not completely without pitch. If a broom handle is dropped on a hard floor, most people would classify the resultant sound as noise. The wooden or metal handle probably has a natural frequency and the sound produced would be a definite pitch surrounded by a number of less definite pitches. The percussion section of an orchestra generally creates sounds described as noise. Much of the basis for rhythm seems predicated upon the presence or absence of regular pulses

> **NOISE: Complex sounds which are not periodic and contain overtones which are not part of the natural harmonic series, i.e., inharmonic overtones.**
>
> **INHARMONIC OVERTONES: Those frequencies above a fundamental tone which are not a whole-number multiple of the fundamental and therefore, not in the natural harmonic series of that fundamental.**

that are often supplied by clapping hands, beating wooden sticks together, striking drum heads, the striking of metal sheets, etc. Musicians also seem to enjoy punctuating musical phrases with irregular, predetermined pulses of noise, often off the beat. And, in order to enhance the climax of a final cadence, noise is sometimes called for by a composer and added by the percussionist to the final chords in the form of drum rolls and cymbal crashes.[7]

Electronic musicians make use of a particular kind of noise called **white noise** or white sound. If an FM radio is tuned to a place where no station is broadcasting, something approximating white noise will be experienced. White noise consists of random occurrences of all pitches within the audible frequency spectrum at equal amplitude.[8] This sound may be added in varying amounts to musical tones or used alone to obtain certain musical effects. Again, it is important to remind ourselves that some noise is judged by our society as having musical attributes.

When a pianist performs, one hears not only the musical tones produced by the piano but also the pianist's fingers striking the keys, the piano's mechanical action, the felt hammers striking the strings when returning to their rest position, and the action of the pedals. Yet, when heard as a composite performance, one judges the overall effect as being musical. Probably, repeated exposure to these sounds has allowed one to learn that such a composite of music and noise is generally judged to be "musical" in effect.[9]

The articulation of wind instruments is another example of noise that is judged to be musical. The sound of the tongue striking the reed of a clarinet, saxophone, oboe or bassoon is an example of musical noise. The same is true of the brass instrument's attack. And indeed, the initial sound produced when a rosined bow excites a violin string is, in fact, noise. Other forms of musical attack such as pizzicato, slap, tremolo and flutter tongue contain varying combinations of noise and musical tone.

Noise in the Environment

Sounds exist throughout our environment. Usually, they are unpitched and are, by our definition, noise. The name given to the composite of these environmental noises is **ambience** (ambient sound or ambient noise). If one desires quiet, ambience is particularly noticeable. In concert halls, the composite of audience movement, whispers, coughs and air conditioning sounds comprise an ambience that, while not loud in the subjective sense, may cause some to strain to hear the music over it. In cities, traffic sounds and other machine noises have been measured at 80 dB SPL and above. Over a prolonged period, factory work-

---

WHITE NOISE (White Sound): The random occurrence of all pitches at equal amplitude within the audible frequency spectrum. The "hiss" is quite similar to the sound heard between stations on the FM radio band.

AMBIENCE: The composite of sound in a particular environment. Ambience is sometimes thought of as all sounds present except the sounds to which one is trying to attend.

---

[7] *Bartholomew, op. cit., p. 160.*

[8] *Since all frequencies (colors) are present in the visible spectrum in what is described as the color white, white noise gets its name from a similar acoustic occurrence.*

[9] *If the strings on a piano were damped (not allowed to vibrate) and a pianist were to play the instrument anyway, the performance would consist of a great deal of rather obvious noises which are always present, even when the strings are not damped.*

20

ers who are employed near large and noisy machines can damage their hearing apparatus by being subjected to such ambience.[10] Some machines produce noises above 120 dB SPL that is above the pain threshold. Jet planes and rockets are good examples of this kind of machine noisemaker. There are federal standards for limits to exposure to ambient noise levels in the workplace.

Masking

The effect of one set of sounds impinging upon the perception of another set of sounds is referred to as **masking**. The above examples of ambience are some examples. Possibly a more familiar example is the television playing while one is trying to listen to music in another part of the house. The intensity or amplitude of the music must be increased to above the television sound's intensity for one to minimally perceive the music and overcome the masking effect of the television sound. Another common example of masking occurs while listening to music in a car, especially with the windows open. The ambience in this environment consists of the sound of the car's engine, the sound of its tires moving over the road, traffic sounds, and the white noise created by moving the car through the air. Added to this already rich aural environment, people frequently talk to each other while the music is playing. Sometimes masking becomes a distracting influence. It is quite possible to overload the hearing mechanism by masking, so that no other sounds can be perceived.[11] Holding a conversation in a noisy restaurant means you've probably had to raise your voice in order to be heard. You were overcoming what is called the "noise floor," or the "level of ambient noise in that environment."

WAVEFORMS

When analyzing sounds and especially how musical instruments work (Chapter 3), a somewhat more careful study of the creation of the sound waves at their source and how they travel away from that source must be undertaken. To begin, think of a clothesline loosely suspended between two trees. If the line is struck sharply in the center with a stick, energy in the form of two waves will travel away from the point of impact toward both trees. When these traveling waves reach the trees to which the line is tied, the waves will travel back again toward the center. They cross each other (still retaining their original shape) and travel to the opposite tree. This motion will continue, the frequency remaining constant, until the energy of the blow dissipates and the amplitude is no longer evident.

---

[10] Taylor, Rupert, Noise, (Hammondsworth, England: Penguin Books Ltd., 1970), p. 19.

[11] One important example of masking occurs when the heating or air conditioning ducts in school classrooms create ambience with air rushing out of ductwork and/or grills that are too small. This ambient layer of noise often goes unnoticed, yet students talk "within" this masking in order not to be overheard by the teacher. When the teacher does notice, stress is the result. This situation occurs all too often in schools and is probably more prevalent than commonly thought. See: Wagner. M. J. & Ostendorf, P., Music Facilities Design Guidelines for Florida's Public Schools. Office of Educational Facilities, State of Florida, Department of Education, 1940 N. Monroe Street, Tallahassee, Florida, 32303, 1993.

> **MASKING: The process by which the threshold of audibility of one set of sounds is raised by the presence of another set of sounds. The amount of masking effect is usually expressed in decibels.**

Figure 2-6. A traveling wave.

Standing Waves

If the above experiment is performed again, but if this time the line is repeatedly struck at exactly the same location in the middle and at regular intervals of time at one of the line's resonant frequencies, the waves traveling back and forth will soon begin to look as if they are standing still. The regular and repeated displacement of the line will create **standing waves**. The energy creating these waves is not static or standing still, but regular displacement of the line causes the waves to appear motionless in a pattern similar to the illustration in Figure 2-7. This waveform will most probably be complex and will be comprised of more than just a fundamental frequency.

STANDING WAVES: When a string is set in motion by regular and repeated excitation, the energy traveling back and forth along its length produces an appearance that the string is not at rest, yet standing still. The resonant cavities of most musical instruments are built in such a way that when excited, they set up standing waves, with loops in certain places and nodes in others.

Figure 2-7. A standing wave.

22

If the shape of the fundamental standing wave is analyzed, it is easy to see that the points closest to where the line is tied to the trees are relatively free of motion while the center of the line is the point of maximum displacement. When describing standing waves, the point or points of minimum displacement are called **nodes**, and those points of maximum displacement may be referred to as **loops** or antinodes.

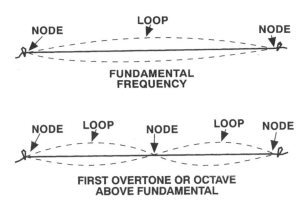

Figure 2-8. First Overtone or Octave Above Fundamental.

Transverse Waves

Standing waves propagate energy (disturb the medium; in this case, air) in an area 360 degrees around the line. Disturbances in the form of **transverse waves** move away from the vibrating line at right angles to it, in all three dimensions. These waves are called transverse because they are propagated (transmitted) at right angles to the sound source. They travel away from the line as a series of **compressions** and **rarefactions** through the air.

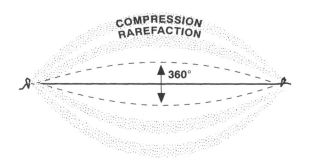

Figure 2-9. Transverse waves traveling away from a vibrating string.

NODES: Points of minimum displacement in sound waves.

LOOPS: Points of maximum displacement in sound waves. Sometimes these are called antinodes.

TRANSVERSE WAVES: Waves in which the molecules of the transmitting medium were disturbed at right angles to the sound source. Some examples are waves produced by a tuning fork, waves on the surface of the water when a stone is dropped in, waves produced by vibrating strings and those made by vocal folds.

Longitudinal Waves

Sound waves propagated into the air in the same direction as the vibration of the sound source are called **longitudinal waves**.[12] To visualize longitudinal waves, one might think of a coiled spring loosely contained in a cylinder or pipe. If the cylinder were given a sharp blow at one end, a traveling wave of compression generated into the spring would move away from the blow. The spring would move back and forth in accordance with the laws of elasticity and momentum. Repeatedly applying blows to the end of the cylinder, at regular intervals and at one of the spring's resonant frequencies, would create a standing wave. That is, points of compression and areas of rarefaction would appear to be standing still at points along the spring. This is in effect what happens when vibrating air molecules enclosed in a cylinder are set into regular vibration.

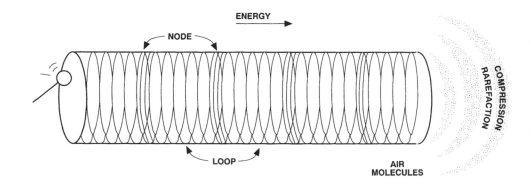

Figure 2-10. Longitudinal waves traveling away from a closed pipe.

As the sound energy leaves the source (the air in the cylinder), the air at the end of the pipe is excited and travels away in an ever-widening progression of compressions and rarefactions. The next chapter will illustrate how these acoustic events occur in musical instruments.

LONGITUDINAL WAVES: Waves in which the molecules of the transmitting medium are disturbed in the same direction as the sound source. Some examples are sound from air columns and sound waves through solids.

[12] *While differences between transverse and longitudinal waves cannot be heard, it seems important that an introduction to musical acoustics contain some explanation of whether a disturbance is propagated transversely through the air by vibrating strings, bars, plates and/or membranes or by the periodic throttling of an air column which produces longitudinal waves, as in the case of wind instruments.*

DISCUSSION QUESTIONS FOR CHAPTER TWO

1. Describe what is meant by tone color, quality, or timbre of a sound.

2. Describe some very fine aural discriminations that show the acuity of our timbre judgments.

3. Discuss what a violin string might sound like if everything else remained constant, but the body of the instrument was removed.

4. Draw a graph of the envelope you hear for a piano tone, a trumpet's attack, a violin's legato attack, a bass drum struck once.

5. Discuss the advantages and disadvantages of noise. Do you think that the frequency or pitch of noise matters?

6. Describe the relationship between ambient classroom noise and off-task student behavior.

7. What are the differences between transverse and longitudinal waves? Do these differences matter to our ears?

Acoustic Properties of String, Wind and Percussion Music Instruments

CHAPTER 3

ACOUSTIC CLASSIFICATION OF TRADITIONAL MUSIC INSTRUMENTS

Because acoustical musical instrument families have certain common acoustical elements, we will study the physical elements common to all instruments of a particular family rather than study each instrument separately. **Stringed instruments** are musical instruments whose sound source is a stretched, vibrating string over a resonating air chamber. **Wind instruments** use as a sound source either an **edge tone** or a reed mechanism that produces periodic puffs of air and resonates a column of air. **Percussion instruments** are classified as instruments having as a sound source either vibrating membranes or vibrating solid bodies.[1] Of course, within each classification or family of instruments, there are properties inherent to each individual instrument. General acoustical elements common to each family will be discussed as well as individual differences between instruments.

STRINGED INSTRUMENTS

Instruments that use vibrating, stretched strings as a sound source are considered members of the string family of instruments. There are three ways in which strings may be caused to vibrate, thereby producing their characteristic sound: **bowing**, as is the usual case with the violin, viola, violoncello and double bass; **plucking**, as with the harp, guitar, mandolin, harpsichord, banjo and the violin family when playing "pizzicato;" and **striking,** the method used to excite the strings of the piano (more properly called the pianoforte). Common to the entire string family are vibrating, stretched strings, and the necessity for these strings to have a resonant air chamber nearby to amplify their sound. The acoustic principles involved in the excitation of strings by the above three methods will be discussed first. Then a closer look at each instrument of the string family and how its individual characteristics help determine its resultant sound can be better understood.

Bowing

When horsehair on the bow that has been coated with rosin[2] is pulled across a violin string made of either metal, nylon or catgut, the string is engaged

---

[1] *After Culver, Charles A., Musical Acoustics, (New York: McGraw-Hill Book Company, 1969).*

[2] *Rosin is obtained from the sap or pitch of pine trees. It is processed by heat to the proper consistency (somewhere between crystalline and sticky). If it is too dry, it will not stick to the horsehair of the bow, thus decreasing the friction between the bow and the string. If it is too sticky, it will coat the string, thus inhibiting vibration.*

> **STRINGED INSTRUMENTS:** Instruments whose sound source is a stretched vibrating string over a resonating body containing an air chamber.
>
> **WIND INSTRUMENTS:** Instruments whose sound source is either an edge tone or a reed mechanism to resonate a column of air.
>
> **EDGE TONES:** Vibration caused by eddies of air which are produced by a stream of air blown across the edge of a plate. These eddies curl first one way, then the other. It is these changes in air direction that are the sound source.
>
> **PERCUSSION INSTRUMENTS:** Instruments having as a sound source either a vibrating membrane or vibrating solid bodies.

by the friction of the bow hair and pulled out of position momentarily. When the tension on the string becomes greater than the friction can bear, the string snaps back and, because of its elasticity and momentum, overshoots its point of rest. As the bow hair again engages the string, the whole process begins again. The string is caused to vibrate at its natural frequency; one that depends upon its composition, its thickness, its length and the amount of tension on it. The string's length is determined by the placement of the player's fingers upon the string (the shorter the vibrating length, the higher the pitch). When looking temporally (through time) at the first few microseconds of a bow stroke, some interesting phenomena are revealed. At the beginning of the bow stroke or initial attack, the excitation sends traveling waves to both ends of the string, that return and set up the familiar standing wave pattern. But because the violin string is usually not bowed in the middle of the string, but nearer the bridge, these traveling waves produce momentary high overtones due to the unevenness of the traveling waves. This very momentary process gives the initial attack of the string its own characteristics, and sometimes the squeaky sound we hear when first learning to play the instrument.

As was discussed in Chapter 2, the initial vibration of the string is longitudinal until a standing wave is created. At the moment the standing wave is created, transverse waves, at right angles to the string's length, are propagated into the air by the vibrating string. As the bow pulls the string out of rest position it also twists it slightly, thereby creating a small amount of **torsional vibration**. Torsional vibration is neither transverse nor longitudinal, but helps to form the particular complexities of vibration that influence the strength of the overtones produced. The bow draws the string away from its point of rest at a slower rate than the string snaps back, that also helps form the particular harmonic pattern. This harmonic pattern is composed of a number of overtones that we recognize as a bowed string's tone. Sounds that are generated by slower displacement than the return, are called "sawtooth" waveforms (a name taken from the shape of the graph formed by their vibrations).[3] A further discussion of sawtooth waveforms will take place in Chapter 11.

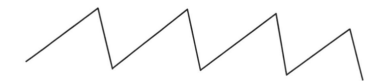

Figure 3-1. A graph of the vibration pattern of a bowed string.

TORSIONAL VIBRATION: To-and-fro movement in two dimensions with a twisting direction motion of the vibrating body in the third dimension.

[3] Olsen, Harry F., Musical Engineering, (New York: McGraw-Hill Book Company, 1952), pp. 121-122.

Plucking

When a string is plucked, it is excited only initially. After the initial excitation, the tone begins immediately to "decay" or become softer. That is, after the initial excitation the amplitude becomes less and less because the "S" and "R" components of the ADSR envelope are manipulated to have extremely short durations. Some of the same rules that apply to bowed sounds are relevant to how a plucked string produces its sound. Traveling wave motion creates standing waves that, in turn, propagate transverse waves into the surrounding media. But there are also differences. If the finger is used to pluck the string, the traveling wave will be less angular than it would be if the string were plucked with a sharper or harder object like the fingernail or the plectrum on a harpsichord. The more angular the traveling wave, the more overtones will be excited. Sounds made by plucking are always loudest at the point just after the attack and then decay at a rate commensurate with the characteristics of the string and the resonant bodies that are near it.

Striking

Struck strings produce sounds with characteristics similar to those of plucked strings. The harder the felt on the hammers of a piano, the more angular the traveling wave and consequently, the more complex the vibration. Piano tones are usually judged as pleasing when the sound is not too harmonically complex. The "honky-tonk" effect produced by extremely hard or old felt hammers can be reduced by pricking the hammers with a pin at the point where they come into contact with the piano strings. This procedure loosens the fibers of the felt and will permit a more rounded traveling wave when the strings are struck. Consequently, a less complex attack will result.

A common technique is to slap the string of an acoustic or electric bass so that the string is forced into contact with the fingerboard or fret. This produces a sound with an extremely loud and complex attack (AD), almost no sustain (S) and a very quick release (R).

ACOUSTIC PROPERTIES OF STRINGED INSTRUMENTS

Although it is important to know that the method of excitation of a string can help determine the timbre of the sound, it is also important to note that other characteristics inherent to each individual instrument help determine the characteristic sound it will produce. The string family can be divided into two subgroups: instruments where the length of the string is changed by the player's fingers (violin, viola, violoncello, double bass, guitar, mandolin, etc.) and instruments whose strings are of a fixed length (pianoforte, harp and harpsichord).[4]

---

[4] *A number of sources are available which more thoroughly illuminate the area of "acoustic properties of musical instruments." Some of these sources are listed below:*

Backus, John, The Acoustic Foundations of Music, (New York: W. W. Norton Book Company, 1969).

Bartholomew, Wilmer T., Acoustics of Music, (Englewood Cliffs, New Jersey, Prentice-Hall, Inc., 1964).

Culver, op. cit.

Olsen, op. cit.

Taylor, C.A., The Physics of Musical Sound, (New York: American Elsevier Publishing Company, 1966).

Instruments with Strings of Changing Length

Instruments with strings whose length is changed by the placement of the fingers have certain features in common. Each has a neck or fingerboard, a resonant body under the strings, a nut and a bridge that suspends the strings over the fingerboard and body of the instrument, and at least one opening in the body that allows the resonant air to be vented.

In these variable-length stringed instruments, vibrations generated by the strings are modified by the characteristics of the bridge; the shape and size of the "F hole" or opening in the body of the instrument; the position of the sound post (whose purpose it is to transmit the vibration of the belly and the bridge directly to the back of the instrument); what is used to change the length of the string; and the various combinations of these factors. The shape and size of the instrument's body also modify and amplify the timbre of the tone produced by the strings.

Because of differences in thickness and composition, no two strings produce exactly the same waveform. Other factors are also important in the composite final string sound. Some components that must be considered when analyzing the musical tone of a stringed instrument include whether the string is excited with a downbow or an upbow, the speed of the bow, the point along the string's length at which the bow or finger excited the string, and the angle and weight of the bow on the string and the physical properties of the bow itself.

Those unpleasant, "squeaky" sounds often produced by beginning string players are caused when the string is stroked lengthwise by the bow rather than directly across it. Instead of producing transverse wave motion, the string is set into longitudinal vibration and the resultant sounds are high-pitched, "squeaky," and often irritating.

Upper harmonics can be eliminated from the string's complex waveform if the string is excited at a point where a node should exist. No node can exist at the point where the string is initially excited, because the act of bowing makes this a point of maximum displacement. Generally strings on members of the violin family are excited at a point somewhere between one-ninth and one-twelfth of the string's vibrating length. Consider the change in timbre if the string were excited at its midpoint, where a node normally occurs for all even-numbered harmonics. If a string were excited at this point, all even-numbered harmonics would either be eliminated or severely reduced because a loop would be created where a node normally exists. On the other hand, if, instead of displacing the string at the point where a node is expected to occur, the string were touched lightly with the finger and excited in the usual manner, the particular harmonic for that length would sound. String players call such tones **artificial harmonics**. By using these artificial harmonics, string players can produce notes that are quite high (and relatively free of overtones) without shortening the length of the string to a point where the fingers must be placed very near the end of the fingerboard. In string literature, rarely are artificial harmonics demanded beyond the third or fourth harmonic. It is necessary that players practice these tones very carefully, because

ARTIFICIAL HARMONICS: Tones produced on stringed instruments by lightly touching a point along the string's length as it is bowed where a node exists.

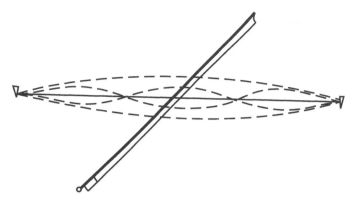

Figure 3-2. Bowing at the midpoint of a string eliminates even-numbered harmonics.

if the string is not stopped at exactly the correct nodal point, either another harmonic will be produced, or all vibration of the string will be suppressed (**damping**)[5] by the player's finger, and no tone will ensue.

If a piece of rubber, wood, or metal (called a mute) is affixed to the bridge of the stringed instrument, less intense tones will result. By restricting the vibration of the bridge the mute decreases the amplitude of the vibration, thus making the tone sound softer. The strength of upper overtones is also diminished (damped).

Some stringed instruments, including the guitar and mandolin, have raised metal bands at certain pre-measured points along the fingerboard. These bands are called **frets**. When the finger depresses the string between the frets, it is the fret instead of the fingers that stops the string and measures the vibrating length of the string. The fret, narrower and harder than the finger, also helps determine the harmonic content of the initial attack and the ensuing decay.

Instruments with Strings of Fixed Length

Instruments whose strings are of fixed length, tension, and thickness have certain characteristics in common. The strings are affixed to a frame called a harp. The lower strings are usually made of copper wire wound around a steel wire core. This type of lower string is more elastic than pure, thick steel strings would be, and thus has more ability to sustain tones. In the case of the pianoforte, loudness is controlled by the weight of the blow of the finger. Through a system of levers, the force of the blow from the finger upon the piano key determines the force of the blow from the hammer to the strings. As is also the case with the plucked string, the initial sound is louder than any portion of the sustained sound. If the pianist wishes to damp the strings after they have been excited and thus stop the tones, he may do so be releasing the keys or by releasing a foot pedal mechanism that moves felt dampers onto all the strings at once. In order for the piano to produce sounds loud enough to be heard comfortably, the upper notes have three strings tuned to each pitch. A pedal is provided that can move the row of hammers slightly off center so that if a prolonged soft passage is called for, the hammers will strike only two of the three strings.

DAMPING: Suppression of vibration by applying physical restraint. Decrease in amplitude due to interfering forces.

FRETS: Metal inlays in the fingerboard of some stringed instruments. Frets are placed perpendicularly to the strings at pre-measured places along the length of the fingerboard to fix the length of the string when the finger presses behind them.

---

[5] *Sometimes this is erroneously referred to as "dampening." The object is not moistened, but rather, having its vibration inhibited.*

Some pianos are built with harps that stand upright and some with harps that are laid horizontally (called grand pianos). Grand pianos usually have longer strings than uprights, necessitating a horizontal placement of the harp. The longer the strings, the longer a tone will sustain. Of course, the longer the string (with thickness remaining constant), the more tension it must have to sound at a particular pitch. The largest concert grand pianos have a total string tension of approximately thirty tons.

The sounding board reinforces the tone of the piano's strings by resonating sympathetically and exciting transverse vibration of the surrounding air. In order to reinforce and amplify the broadest possible spectrum of sound, the sounding board is slightly arched.

Because the highest strings of the piano are quite short and must be stretched so tightly, their elasticity is somewhat reduced. A piano's high tones do not sustain nearly as long as its low tones, due to the difference in tension and length of the strings; consequently dampers are not needed for the instrument's extreme high register.

WIND INSTRUMENTS

Instruments that produce sound by exciting air encased in a rigid pipe are members of the wind family of instruments. The air column may be caused to vibrate in two ways: edge tones and **reeds**. Flutes and certain organ pipes produce sound using edge tones. Reeds are used on other woodwind instruments (oboe, bassoon, clarinet, saxophone). On "brasswind" instruments (trumpet, French horn, trombone, baritone horn, tuba and euphonium) buzzing lips are used as a sort of reed mechanism. Acoustically, the human voice can be considered a reed wind instrument.

The wind family of instruments may be divided into two subgroups by a simple acoustical principle—whether or not the instrument is made of a pipe open at both ends (called open pipes) or at only one end (called stopped pipes). Generally, open pipes depend upon edge tones as a sound source and stopped pipes depend upon either a reed or the lips (acting as a reed) as a sound source.[6]

Edge Tones and Open Pipes

Open pipes are excited into vibration by edge tones. To illustrate how edge tones are produced, remember what happens to water when one's hand is quickly dragged or pulled through it. Just as little whirlpools, called vortices or eddies, will be formed in and near the hand's path through the water, these vortices will be formed behind rocks or obstacles in a river or stream.

This is also the case when air is blown across the edge of an opening in a pipe (for instance, the mouth of a bottle). Vortices form first above (and behind)

REEDS: Any object or pair of objects which, when vibrated at the closed end of a pipe, sets the air in the pipe into vibration.

[6] See note #4.

the obstacle, in this case the lip of the bottle, and then below. As the rapid alteration of these vortices or whirlwinds passes near the air contained within the bottle, they excite it into vibration first as a traveling wave and subsequently as a standing wave, much as the initial excitation of a string. The rate at which vortices are formed (frequency) is determined by the velocity of the air blown across the opening, not by the length of the pipe, although after a standing wave is formed a coupling of the two does occur.

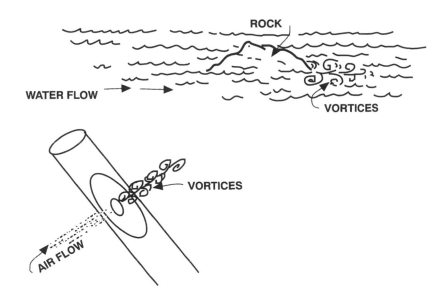

Figure 3-3. Vortices formed in water behind a rock in a stream and vortices formed behind the rear edge of a flute mouthpiece.

Edge tones are inherently of low intensity (amplitude) and have quite high frequencies. They are not usually heard as part of the tone produced. They are, nevertheless, the sound source of tones produced by open pipes. Interestingly, the air enclosed in open pipes vibrates so easily and freely (excitation) that the frequency of the edge tone does not have to be very close to the pipe's resonant frequency for it to sound an audible tone. What is heard is the resonant air column sounding at a frequency and timbre determined first by the frequency of the edge tone and then by the size and shape of the pipe. That is, the frequency of the traveling wave is determined solely by the speed of the air blown across the opening, while the standing wave's frequency is determined both by the speed of the air and the internal dimensions of the pipe. A node will form at the center of the pipe and a loop will fit into the ends. A node cannot physically occur at the open end of a pipe. Because of this physical limitation on vibration within a pipe, the actual wavelength of the fundamental frequency of a pipe open at both ends is twice the length of the pipe, since this is the distance required to complete one full cycle of vibration. Figure 3-4 illustrates the length of the pipe compared to the wavelength of the fundamental tone. Actually, physicists have determined that the loops formed by the vibrating air column occur just beyond the ends of the pipe. Furthermore, whether the openings of the pipe are at the physical extremities of the pipe or somewhere along its length, as in the case of the flute

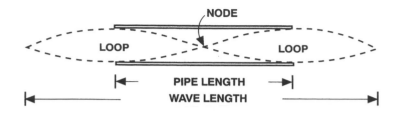

Figure 3-4. A standing wave in a pipe open at both ends. The wave length is approximately twice the length of the pipe.

(Figure 3-5), the actual length of the air column is determined by the distance between the sound source and the closest opening. The pitch produced by an open pipe may be lowered in two ways—either by increasing the pipe's length or by increasing its diameter. The pipe may be a perfect cylinder, as is the flute, it may be square, as are some wooden organ pipes, or even other shapes. The shape of the **bore** (inside diameter of the pipe) will mainly affect the overtones. The overall volume of air contained within the pipe is actually the main determinant of fundamental frequency or pitch of the tone produced.

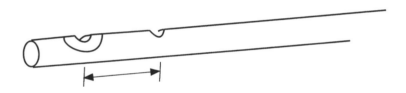

Figure 3-5. A stylization of the effective length of the air column for an open C# on a flute.

Reeds and Stopped Pipes

Either single or double reeds can act as a sound source. As air is blown through a double reed, it vibrates both longitudinally and transversely, alternately opening and closing the elliptical opening between the reeds. These pulsations give rise to a series of compressions and rarefactions within the pipe. In the case of the single reed, air blown past the reed that is affixed to a mouthpiece excites the reed into both longitudinal and transverse vibration. The reed's beating against the slightly smaller mouthpiece opening, alternately opening and almost closing the pipe, thus gives rise to a series of compressions and rarefactions (puffs of air) moving through the pipe as a traveling wave.

Without stretching the imagination too far, it is possible to visualize the human vocal folds as well as the lips (used as the sound source on brasswinds) as vibrating double reeds, both operating in much the same manner as double reeds made of cane. Of course, due to differences in their composition and vibrating characteristics, the sound source of brasswind instruments and the hu-

---

BORE: The inside shape and dimensions of a wind instrument.

man voice is somewhat different than the wooden-cane sound source of wood-wind instruments.[7]

Because the sound source (reed) is at the closed end of the pipe, as the instrument is played a node is formed at this closed end in the resultant standing wave. The rate of opening and closing of the reed (traveling wave) is determined by the speed of the air blown across it. That is, the rate of the reed's vibration is determined first by the speed of air and when the standing wave is formed, and then by the internal dimensions of the stopped pipe. The reed is then coupled with the air column to determine the pitch of the tone produced. If the speed of the air is increased beyond the limits of this coupled system, the next higher overtone is produced. Woodwind players refer to these tones as "squeaks," that are quite common with beginners. If a tone is played on the head joint of a flute, then the end closed and played again, the tone from the closed (or stopped) pipe will be lower by nearly an octave than the tone of the open pipe. Remember, in an open pipe, physical laws necessitate having a loop at both ends of the pipe. In an open pipe, the wavelength will be twice the length of the pipe. In a stopped pipe the same set of physical laws apply—open end, a loop; closed end, a node. The resultant wavelength must be four times the length of the stopped pipe (See Figure 3-6). Because a node cannot form at the open end of a stopped pipe (more properly called a

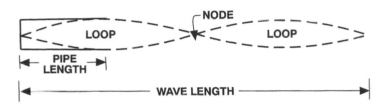

Figure 3-6. A standing wave in a closed pipe. The standing wave is approximately four times the length of the pipe.

stopped cylinder, as we will see in the next section), the second harmonic, or octave of the fundamental, is a physical impossibility. This theoretical octave would need a node at the open end of the pipe (See Figure 3-7). Instead, the third harmonic is heard (a twelfth above the fundamental). This is indeed the case with

Figure 3-7.

--------- **Theoretically impossible second harmonic (an octave above the fundamental)**

——————— **Third harmonic (a twelfth above the fundamental)**

---

[7] *There is some reason to believe that a more accurate illustration of the action of brasswind player's lips might be the single reed, because often one lip may actually travel through space more than another.*

the clarinet. It produces a twelfth when its lower register is overblown. However, waveform analysis shows that certain other even-numbered harmonics (odd-numbered partials) are present in the clarinet's overtone series, though they are of an appreciably lower intensity. It is, therefore, not a true stopped pipe.

ACOUSTIC PROPERTIES OF WIND INSTRUMENTS

So far in this survey of wind instruments, differentiations have been made between open and stopped pipes, single and double reeds, and kinds of reeds used by woodwinds, brasswinds, and the human voice. One other delineation is very important. As was previously stated, if a pipe is a cylinder then it behaves as either an open or stopped pipe depending upon where the air is introduced and whether or not an edge tone or a reed is the sound source. If, however, the shape of a stopped pipe is conical, then it will behave in the same manner as an open pipe even though it is stopped at one end. The saxophone family has conical bores, as do the oboe and bassoon. All brasswinds are shaped conically along some portion of their length. Because of their conical bore, all these instruments are capable of producing the octave above the fundamental and all overtones in the harmonic series. An examination of how different pitches are produced in woodwind and brasswind instruments is the next order of business.

Woodwinds

In all woodwinds, holes are drilled at pre-measured points along the length of the instrument so that the production of chromatic half steps is possible. The distance between the sound source (either the tone hole or reed) and the first open hole is the effective or "speaking length" of the pipe. Some holes cannot be comfortably covered because the hole is in an out-of-the way place for the fingers. In these cases, a system of levers, called keys, are manipulated by the fingers and make pads close and seal the holes.

A vent hole is provided on woodwind instruments to facilitate playing either an octave or, in the case of the clarinet, the twelfth, by reducing the air pressure on the air column. In order for woodwinds to play notes higher than their second range (made possible by the vent hole), a rather complicated and ingenious system of cross fingerings has been devised.[8]

Frequency range plays an important role in all woodwinds. Lower registers have an audibly different timbre than the middle and upper registers, due to the amount of selective reinforcement at certain frequency ranges. These general-frequency range differences are the result of formants.[9]

---

[8] *Most woodwind methods contain fingering charts which may be used to discover "third range" cross-fingerings. The flutist, Theobold Bohm (1794-1881) is credited with developing the modern system of keying the flute and clarinet. Duplicate fingerings in this system help facilitate musical passages which before were impossible.*
Apel, Willi, "Bohm System," Harvard Dictionary of Music, *second edition, (Cambridge, Mass.: The Belknap Press of Harvard University Press, 1969), p. 99.*
Bohm, T., "An Essay on the Construction of Flutes," (1882).

[9] *see pg.16, Chapter 2*

Brasswinds

Most brasswinds have three valves that open and close various pipes along the length of the instrument. Valves are either pistons that move up and down, opening one pipe while closing another, or rotary (pivoted on an axis) valves that serve the same function. While seven combinations of pipe lengths are possible (including open horn or no depressed valves), brasswind players depend heavily upon the natural harmonic series in order to change tones. In fact, the fundamental tones of brasswind instruments are produced only with great difficulty. Their useable range begins with the first overtone. The trombone has no valves, but the length of its pipe is changed by the use of a slide.

Bending or curving the pipe of a brasswind instrument has little, if any, effect upon the tone produced. This might be especially gratifying to brass players whose instruments would be unmanageable if pipe lengths had to be maintained in a straight line to produce tones. In brasses, the flare of the bell helps to suppress the upper harmonics so that the tone is more "mellow." Such a large flare also tends to reduce the possibility of the pipe resonating at its natural frequency. Instead, a broad band of frequencies is resonated and dispersed by the bell, some even back into the instrument.

The Human Voice

The frequency of the human voice is controlled by the thickness, length, and amount of tension on the vocal folds. Two folds of membrane partially cover the **trachea** or "windpipe" forming the **glottis**. These vocal folds may be thought of as a double-reed mechanism because they function in somewhat the same manner. As air from the lungs is forced upward through the glottis, the folds are literally blown apart—upward, outward and into vibration. The tone produced with the vocal folds above, without complicated resonators, is an extremely weak yet complex buzzing sound. The cavities that lie above the glottis form the resonating chamber. These include the laryngeal cavity, the pharynx, the oral cavity, the sinus cavities and other hollow spaces contained within the head. The oral cavity is the most flexible of these resonators and, consequently, modification if its size and shape produces the most significant vocal effects and changes. The pharynx, the largest of the resonators, interacts with the oral cavity to produce formants. A mature male voice sounds approximately one octave lower than either a female or the immature (child's) voice because male vocal folds thicken at maturity. Formants in the male voice have been found between 400 and 600 Hz and between 2400 and 3200 Hz. Formants in the female voice lie somewhat higher.[10]

As the throat and mouth change setting for different vowel and consonant sounds, they also change the harmonic content of the vocalization. Consonant sounds are formed more forward in the mouth than vowel sounds. Whispering occurs when the vocal folds are not excited into vibration. The vocal folds

TRACHEA: The "windpipe" or tube from the lungs to the throat and mouth. The vocal folds lie at the top and across the trachea forming the glottis.

GLOTTIS: The opening between the vocal folds.

---

[10] *Backus, op. cit., p. 213.*

  See also:

  Hoops, R.A., Speech Science: Acoustics in Speech, (Springfield, Illinois: C. C. Thomas Books, 1972).
  Colton, R.H., Casper, J.K., Leonard, R. (2005) Understanding Voice Problems: A Physiological Perspective for Diagnosis and Treatment, 3rd ed. Baltimore: Lippincott Williams & Wilkins.

remain in a relaxed position while air is forced through the glottis into the mouth and throat. The mouth and throat then form the vowel and consonant positions required for speech.

While the vocal folds as a sound source may be more closely associated with the operation of double reeds, there is some evidence that high female vocal singing and the male falsetto voice may excite the vocal folds more in the manner that strings are excited. Instead of forcing the folds of tissue fully open then closed, the air seems to act much like a bow, causing the folds to vibrate without closing fully.[11]

PERCUSSION INSTRUMENTS

Instruments using stretched strings and wind instruments produce overtones that are identical in frequency to the harmonic series based upon whatever fundamental is produced. In the case of most percussion instruments, the overtones are generally inharmonic. The frequencies of these inharmonic overtones are not whole-number multiples of the fundamental frequency. These sounds are said to contain a large noise content. Percussion instruments are usually struck. One way to classify this group of instruments is to group them according to pitched versus unpitched instruments. It should be noted that even though the above idea is apparently contradicted (i.e., that noise is a large part of the sound of struck percussion instruments), even pitched percussion instruments contain a number of inharmonic overtones. For our study, three categories of percussion instruments will be delineated based upon their particular acoustic qualities. They are: stretched membranes or drums; vibrating rods such as the tuning fork, triangle, and xylophone; and vibrating plates like the cymbal, gong or bells.[12]

Stretched Membranes

If one were to sprinkle sand evenly across the head of a drum, then excite the head by a sine wave source in the vicinity, the grains of sand would rearrange themselves according to the loops and nodes that were created by the drum head's sympathetic vibration. In most cases, these "acoustic pictures," arranged by the drum head's vibration, are very interesting and even geometrically beautiful. As one would expect, points of maximum vibration (loops) will throw off the sand grains and leave a gathering of particles at the points of least vibration (nodes). These "pictures" are called Chladni figures (pronounced Klad-knee) and are named after the man who first described them (See Figure 3-8).

The conditions under which drum heads generate sound are very similar to those conditions that cause strings to produce tones. Thickness, tension, and size contribute to the quality of the tone produced. The head is under tension

---

[11] *Bartholomew, op. cit., p. 142.*

[12] *See note #4.*

Figure 3-8. A Chladni figure created with sand on a vibrating metal plate. Likely the plate was excited by bowing it at its edge.

around its circumference which gives it elasticity. Its pitch is determined by the thickness of the membrane and the tension under which it is stretched. Its intensity is determined by the force of the blow. The timbre produced is modified by the kind of striker used (wood, felt, etc.), compositional characteristics of the drum head, the sharpness of the blow, and where on the head the drum is struck. If a node is struck, little vibration will be transmitted to the rest of the head and the tone will be somewhat damped.

Vibrating Rods

Rods may be likened to stretched strings, in that the nature of the movements of a vibrating stretched string and a vibrating metal or wooden rod are quite similar. Rods need not be stretched however, because they have inherent elasticity. When a rod is struck, transverse vibration occurs and loops form at both ends (if the rod is free to vibrate at both ends). Figure 3-9 shows the fundamental and first overtone of a vibrating rod. Notice that no odd overtones can be present because the ends of the rod always form loops. Rods are capable of longitudinal and even torsional vibration if the rod is stroked in a particular manner. Generally, they are struck. The tuning fork is an example of a vibrating rod (though bent into a "U" shape). The tuning fork gives a rather pure tone, and those overtones that do exist are weak, have high frequencies, and are inharmonic. Another example of vibrating rods are the claves. Their pitch is not very definite and the overtones produced are strong and inharmonic.

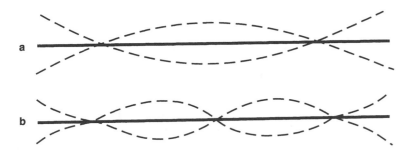

Figure 3-9. Rods vibrating at the (a) fundamental and (b) second harmonic.

Vibrating Plates

Plates are similar to rods in that they do not require stretching to be inherently elastic. They also resemble stretched membranes because, when struck or bowed at their edge, Chladni figures appear. Loops tend to form on the outside edges (if free) and very intricate and complicated patterns of loops and nodes may be noted (see Figure 3-8). Plates are capable of an almost infinite number of vibration patterns. Cymbals are one example of vibrating plates; bells are another. Bells may be thought of as bent plates, much as the tuning fork may be thought of as a bent rod.

ACOUSTIC PROPERTIES OF PERCUSSION INSTRUMENTS

Percussion instruments are many and of widely diverse construction. A common characteristic shared by all is a general inability to produce overtones of the same harmonic series as the fundamental tone. Stretched membranes, vibrating rods and vibrating plates offer one kind of classification for percussion instruments; whether percussion instruments are pitched or unpitched represents another kind of classification.

Stretched Membranes

Unpitched, stretched membranes are used on the snare drum. The batter head is struck. Its motion excites the air in the cylinder into vibration that in turn excites the snare head. The stretched snares are similarly excited but are also affected by their own tension. They move away from the snare head and then snap back, causing a second percussive sound to follow just after the first. This sound is transmitted back to the batter head making the composite sound a rather sharp, loud, yet indefinite noise. Snares may be loosened and consequently disengaged from the snare head if a tom-tom effect is required. The snare drum is provided with a set of screws around the diameters of both the batter and the snare head so that the tension of the heads may be adjusted. There is a small hole in the cylinder (or body) of the snare drum to allow a vent for the air that is momentarily compressed when the batter head is struck. Wooden and sometimes plastic, fiberglass, or metal sticks are used to play the snare drum. The shell of the drum, itself, may be made from a variety of materials and adds to the harmonic complexities of the drum's sound.

The bass drum is a large version of the snare drum, but without snares. It is usually played with a stick, the end of which is covered with cotton wadding wrapped in sheepskin or other damping material. This kind of beater gives the tone a less definite attack and consequently a less complex sound. When the bass drum is played out of doors, wooden mallets are often substituted to "crisp" the attack, produce higher harmonics and allow the sound that is produced to travel further.

Tympani, or kettle drums, have a pedal attached to a mechanism that allows the head to be tightened or loosened (and the pitch subsequently raised or lowered) more quickly than the screw mechanism used on the snare drums. The "kettle," or elliptical shape of the resonating chamber, reinforces a rather definite pitch produced by the drum head. The tympani is struck with a soft beater, and pitches, while not as definite as wind or string instruments, are tuned by the timpanist using the foot pedal. Timpanists may be directed to play upon as many as four or five tympani in one orchestral composition.

Vibrating Rods

Examples of vibrating rods are the triangle and the orchestral chimes. Both of these instruments produce a somewhat weak fundamental and high inharmonic overtones. The triangle is suspended loosely on a string and struck anywhere along its length by a metal beater. The chimes are also suspended by strings or gut but must be struck at the top edge of the cylinders in order for the full range of overtones to be produced. A damping mechanism is provided on the chimes. This is a wooden panel with felt-lined holes through which the chimes hang. When damping is required, the player rocks the wooden panel with his foot until it engages the chimes and damps the sound.

Other vibrating rods made of metal are the celesta, orchestra bells, and glockenspiel. Wooden vibrating rods include the xylophone and marimba. The marimba has a series of tubular resonators suspended below each rod. Each resonator is constructed to resonate maximally at the frequency of the vibrating rod under which it is hung. As a matter of economics, plastic rods or rods made from other compounds have replaced rods made from the more traditional materials. However, this adaptation is usually reserved for "school" or "beginning" instruments.

Vibrating Plates

The cymbals and gong are vibrating plates. Cymbals are either struck together or, like the gong, struck with a stick. Both cymbals and gong have an interesting envelope because the most intense portion of the sound is not at the point of impact. This is especially noticeable when these noisemakers are struck with a stick. The sound grows more intense for a second or two after the instrument has been set into vibration. Then it begins a rather long and gradual decay.

Other members of the percussion family are the castanets, tambourine, sleigh bells, sand paper blocks, wood block, finger cymbals, maracas, guiros, conga, bongo, and many other instruments with very specialized and novel sounds.

DISCUSSION QUESTIONS FOR CHAPTER THREE

1. Discuss why orchestral instruments may be classified acoustically into three groups. What physical properties of the instruments are involved in these classifications?

2. Describe how sounds are produced on stringed instruments. How are they reinforced?

3. Describe how sounds are produced on wind instruments. How are they reinforced?

4. Discuss, acoustically, the statement, "Percussion instruments are the noise-makers of the orchestra."

5. What kind of instrument could be constructed from a length of garden hose? (see: Leopold Mozart, *Concerto for Hosepipe and Orchestra*)

Characteristics of Sound

CHAPTER 4

SOUND IN THE ENVIRONMENT

Thus far, attention has been fully focused on what sound is and how sounds are made. There has been no discussion of the effects of the environment upon sound. Natural environmental factors such as temperature and wind will also affect sound. Whether the sound source or the listener is moving or stationary also has a bearing on sound's perception. Additionally, it is most important to realize that while sounds retain their identities in the presence of other sounds, the environment and our perception can cause some very interesting effects when two or more sets of sound waves are presented simultaneously.

ENVIRONMENTAL EFFECTS UPON SOUND

We do not always hear sounds within the confines of a room. Even though the phenomena about to be discussed are in effect when heard indoors, they happen so quickly that they are not usually perceived. So instead, imagine watching a marching band on a parade field. In this situation temperature variants, obstacles between us and the sound source, distance and wind all affect the sounds that are heard after they leave the sound source (the marching band).

Speed of Sound

All sounds, no matter what their pitch, timbre or dynamic level, will travel through a theoretically homogenous medium at the same rate of speed. Therefore, even though a piccolo may be producing a frequency of 1760 Hz and a tuba a frequency of 110 Hz, the two sounds will travel across the parade field at the same rate. However, sound travels about 892,800 times slower than light.[1] This amazing fact is rarely noticed because most careful listening is done indoors where distances are not very great. Since sound travels relatively rapidly anyway (about 1130 feet per second), there are rarely perceivable differences between what is seen and what is heard. Out-of-doors and in very large halls (cathedrals, for instance), that which is seen gets to the perceiver noticeably sooner than that which is heard. The band may step off and at the same time

---

[1] *If light travels at approximately 186,000 miles per second and sound at 1100 feet per second (at 40° F.) their relationship can be computed using simple arithmetic.*

$$\frac{186{,}000 \text{ miles x } 5280 \text{ (feet per mile)}}{1130 \text{ feet per second}}$$

43

begin playing, yet the sound may not reach the audience until the band has already taken two or three steps. This same problem may exist when attending a concert in a very large hall. The sight of the conductor directing can be an exasperating experience for a musician-listener who sees a conductor's beat and hears the result noticeably later than expected.

At seventy degrees Fahrenheit, sound travels at 1130 feet per second. At thirty-two degrees Fahrenheit it travels at 1085 feet per second.[2] Warm air is less dense than cold air and, consequently, sound travels at a faster rate in warmer air. Therefore, the temperature of the environment in which music is played will also help determine the amount of discrepancy between what is seen and what is heard, though this small amount of difference is more of theoretical interest than practical importance.

Diffusion

As sounds leave their source their **wave fronts** travel through the atmosphere at the speed of sound in an ever-widening area. As the wave front gets larger the energy is spread over an ever-enlarging area. Consequently, the further one is from a sound source, the softer are the sounds due to energy loss. This process of reduction in amplitude over distance is known as **diffusion**. Uniform or even diffusion of sound is nearly a physical impossibility since the air through which sound travels is rarely uniform in density. The friction of one air molecule upon another and friction with the surface of the earth are other factors that help reduce the amplitude of sound waves over distances. Sounds that are above 1000 Hz lose energy somewhat faster than those of lower frequencies. So, when the band is heard on the parade field, it is likely that its sounds are somewhat distorted. Therefore, most overtones and many of the higher fundamentals are lost. For the same reasons, when a neighbor's stereo is playing, what comes through the walls are mainly those frequencies below 1000 Hz. The higher tones have dissipated quickly and what is heard are the low frequencies without their associated higher overtones.

There are other factors that need a bit of explanation to fully illustrate the complexity of sound's diffusion. If higher frequencies are being produced with greater amplitude than lower frequencies, the sound would seem somewhat more normal over a distance. However, since the human ear is most sensitive

---

WAVE FRONTS: The shape or configurations of the component compressions and rarefactions as they diffuse through a medium.

DIFFUSION: The dissipation of sound energy or weakening of wave trains as they travel through a medium.

[2] *Early acousticians calculated the speed of sound in solids, having worked out the speed of sound in air from timing the lapse between seeing a distant flash and hearing the explosion. They then timed the lapse between the two sounds when a very long bar or tube was struck at the far end. The Frenchman Biot first did this in 1808, using an iron pipe one kilometer long! It was necessary to clamp a bell to the far end in order to make the airborne waves audible over this distance. Two gentlemen named Colladon and Sturm did a similar, less comfortable experiment to measure the speed of sound in water. They submerged a large bell and a charge of gunpowder in Lake Geneva, Switzerland, simultaneously sounding one and lighting the other. They then measured the interval between hearing the bell and seeing the flash at a distance, again under water. In all these experiments the timing device was a stopwatch, and the results were not very accurate.*
Taylor, Rupert, Noise, (Hammondsworth, Middlesex, England: Penguin Books Ltd., 1970), p. 35.

between 1000 Hz and 5000 Hz, sounds above and below these frequencies will be perceived less easily. Furthermore, very low tones lose energy faster than medium-range tones. Therefore, over a long distance the marching band's middle frequencies will be heard most easily.[3]

A most interesting historical anecdote having to do with sound diffusion is related by Bartholomew in his acoustics text.

> The most remarkable instance on record of distance traveled (by sound) is that of the eruption of Krakatoa in 1883, which shot up a column of debris seventeen miles high. Sounds from this eruption were heard over a vast area, especially towards the west. They were noticed at Rodriguez, nearly 3000 miles away, at Bangkok (1413 miles), in the Philippines (about 1450 miles), in Ceylon (2058 miles), and in West and South Australia (from 1300 to 2250 miles). And, though we do not have any record of actual sounds being heard farther than these distances, this eruption caused a worldwide disturbance of the atmosphere, made evident by the change in barometric pressure recorded at various stations. This gigantic "sound wave" (for such it really could be called, being an atmospheric pressure variation traveling at a speed comparable with the ordinary velocity of sound), traveled outward from the volcano as a center until it became a great circle enveloping the earth, then on to the other side, diminishing in size until it contracted to a point on the earth diametrically opposite from Krakatoa. This passage around the earth took about 18 hours. The wave was then reflected so that it traveled backward to the volcano, from which it was again sent out in its original direction. In an article in the Eleventh Edition of the *Encyclopedia Britannica*, Sir R. Strachey says: "In this manner its repetition was observed not fewer than seven times at many of the stations, four passages having been those of the wave traveling from Krakatoa, and three passages of those of the wave traveling from its antipodes, subsequently to which its traces were lost." Thus this gigantic sound wave traveled for at least 127 hours. Tremendous water waves were also generated by this eruption, which caused the loss of over 36,000 lives. Some of these (water) waves traveled as far as 8000 miles, or more.[4]

Reflection and Refraction

The reflection, or bouncing back, of sound waves was discussed briefly in Chapter 1. Echoes have been known to cause some curious effects. In round halls, sound seems to cling closely to the walls. Concave (inwardly curved) surfaces tend to focus sound while convex (outwardly curved) surfaces diffuse sound, much as mirrors do with light rays. The angle at which the wave front hits a smooth, flat surface will equal to the angle of its echo or reflection. Even though wave fronts travel in straight lines through a medium, we must keep in mind that in actuality a wave front will have a large curved area of disturbance that is a more accurate picture of what is being reflected (see Figure 4-2).

---

[3] *See figure 1-3.*

[4] *Bartholomew, Wilmer T.,* Acoustics of Music, *(Englewood Cliffs, New Jersey: Prentice-Hall, Inc., 1964), pp. 42-43.*

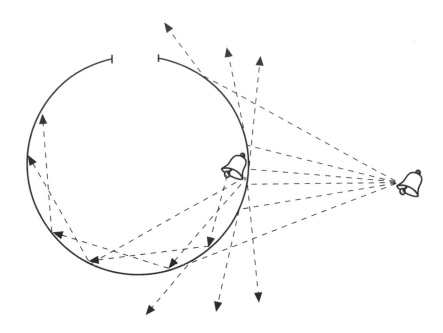

Figure 4-1. Sound reflection inside and outside a circular room or hall.

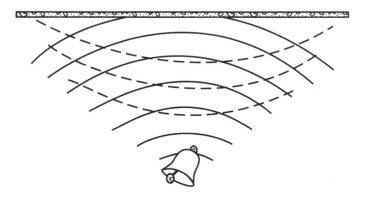

Figure 4-2. A sound wave front being reflected by a straight, hard wall.

The bending of a wave front as it passes through a medium of varying density is called **refraction**. On a cool, dry evening, sound may be refracted (bent) downward as it travels outward from the band on the parade field. As the wave front travels out, away from the sound source, it meets the warmer air lying about the cool evening air. The difference in the atmosphere's density bends the sound waves back toward the earth. The same band playing on a hot, moist afternoon will have its waves bent upward away from the earth, because sound travels faster in warmer air and will therefore tend to lift away from the earth. Therefore, from a distance, the band will be heard more clearly on a cool, dry evening than on a moist, hot afternoon.

REFRACTION: The bending of wave fronts as they pass through media having unequal or varying density.

Wind also refracts sound. Remember, wind is moving air. As a wave front passes through this moving air (the speed of sound is much greater than the speed of wind), it is bent slightly in the direction the wind is traveling. It will be easier to hear the band on the parade field if the wind is blowing toward us than if it is blowing in another direction. (There will, of course, be a bit of masking present as well, due to the white noise also created by the wind.) Sound is bent toward the ground as it moves into the wind and bent away from the ground as it moves in the direction of the wind.

If the band were playing near a body of water the size of a lake or larger, it becomes easier to see why it is more likely that a listener will hear the band clearly at a greater distance. A combination of diffusion, reflection and refraction will skip the sound across the lake. The sound will begin diffusing as it leaves the source. Temperature and wind factors may bend the sound waves back toward the earth, and as the sound waves strike the relatively smooth and hard surface of the water they will be reflected up again as in Figure 4-3.

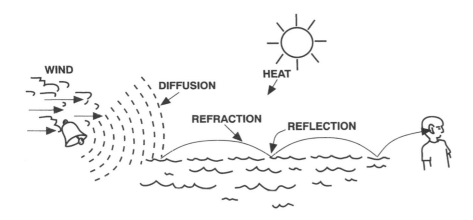

Figure 4-3. As the sound of the bell travels outward, it is _refracted_ downward by the warm temperature of the air, refracted and diffused by the wind, and is _reflected_ upward by the relatively hard surface of the water. Sound can travel great distances across water in this manner.

Diffraction

The spreading of the sound into areas behind and around physical barriers is called **diffraction**. Sound waves tend to "fill in" the areas behind pillars and even walls. The higher the frequency, however, the less the sound will be diffracted. Low tones, on the other hand, diffract quite well. If one goes around the corner of a building, "sound shadows" (not as well defined as light shadows) will occur. Sound does travel around corners, through open windows and seemingly will "fill the room." Only high tones and overtones will be lost. Sound shadows caused by incomplete diffraction of all frequencies may be perceived as lacking complexity due to the resultant loss of overtones. Diffracted sound disperses much as a new sound would; i.e., it diffuses as a sphere, the center of which may be an open window, corner of a building, or obstacle.

DIFFRACTION: The spreading out of wave fronts into areas behind and around physical barriers. Stated another way: the filling-in of areas or spaces behind physical barriers that are blocked and not in a straight line from the sound source.

Doppler Effect

When a police car or ambulance approaches and passes, both the frequency and the amplitude of the siren increase as the vehicle approaches, they reach a peak level at the closest point, and then both decrease as the vehicle passes. This seemingly odd acoustical phenomenon is called the Doppler effect.[5]

It may seem that the nearer we are to a sound, the higher its pitch. Although we know this is not true, if either the sound source or the listener is moving at a sufficient rate, the Doppler phenomenon will be perceived.

The explanation is quite simple. Pitch depends upon the number of vibrations per second that reach the ear. If one moves rapidly toward a sound source or it toward us, the rate at which those vibrations reach us increases. That is, more vibrations reach the ear per second than if both sound source and listener were stationary. The natural consequence of this phenomenon is that a higher pitch is perceived, i.e., one with more vibrations per second.

As the sound source moves away from the listener (or the listener from the sound source), fewer vibrations reach the listener per second and the pitch becomes lower. The relative speed of the sound source or listener is all-important. The distance between the two is not a factor.[6] Distance may seem to play a part because as the sound source and listener get closer and closer, amplitude increases.

To review, the faster the speed that the sound source and listener travel toward or away from each other, the greater the rise or fall in pitch. The rate of movement toward or away from the source of sound is all-important. Distance has only to do with the amplitude of the sound.

SOUND'S EFFECT UPON SOUND

Elements in the natural environment are not the only factors acting upon sound. If more than one sound is present at a time, there are other phenomena that have an effect upon what we hear or perceive. These effects, generally called interference phenomena, include sound reinforcement and cancellation, beats, summation tones and difference tones. Let's examine each separately.

Interference

Whenever more than one sound source is present, there are hundreds of times during the alternation of the natural vibrating periods of each, where reinforcement or cancellation (complete or incomplete) will be the effect. When air is set in motion and numerous waves of compressions and rarefactions exist simultaneously, some of these compressions will momentarily exist together and

---

[5] *The Doppler effect (or Doppler shift), named after Austrian physicist Christian Doppler who proposed its explanation in 1842, is the change in frequency of a wave for an observer moving relative to the source of the waves.*

[6] *Olsen, Harry F., Musical Engineering, (New York: McGraw-Hill Book Company, 1952), p. 13.*

will reinforce each other. When a compression tries to co-exist with a rarefaction, some cancellation of the sound energy occurs, thus decreasing the overall amplitude. If the compression and rarefaction are of different amplitudes or frequencies, they will not completely cancel each other out but will either strengthen or weaken the tone (See Figure 4-4).

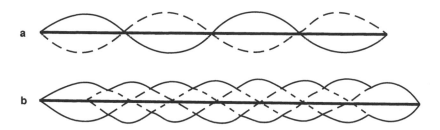

Figure 4-4. (a) Complete and (b) Incomplete cancellation of two tones of the same frequency and amplitude.

"Dead Spots" found in some auditoriums are probably caused by reflected echoes partially cancelling the primary sound. Echoes, having less amplitude than the primary sound, can cause only partial interference and weakening of the resultant sound. For an excellent example of interference one need look only as far as the stereo. If the switches are set so that monophonic music is playing, both speakers, each being a single monophonic source, are creating compressions and rarefactions in exactly the same manner, thus reinforcing each other. If the two wires connected to the terminals on the back of one of the speakers are reversed, the speakers will be "out-of-phase." This simply means that one speaker is one-half cycle ahead of the other. While one speaker is pushing outward and creating a compression, the other is pulling inward and creating a rarefaction. Since the sound being produced by both speakers is exactly the same, but one is one-half cycle ahead of the other, it will readily be determined that there "is a hole" in the sound. While the left speaker will sound to the left and the right speaker will sound to the right, between the speakers very little sound will be heard. This exercise is both an excellent illustration of sound cancellation and a good test to see if stereo speakers are connected properly and "in phase." In the stereo mode, problems will be similar, but not all the sounds on each channel will be exact duplicates of each other. Therefore, the phenomenon just described will not be quite as noticeable. If one has been listening to "out-of-phase" stereo, correcting the problem will give most satisfying musical results.[7]

Audio engineers must always be on the lookout for the possibility of cancellation effect caused by the misplacement of microphones within a sound field. It is possible, when placing multiple microphones in close proximity to one another, to place them so that they pick up sound waves that are out of phase, thus causing cancellation within the signal being recorded or amplified.

---

[7] *With today's "Pro Logic" and "THX" home sound systems, speaker phasing becomes even more important (see Chapter 9, for further explanation).*

Beats

The kind of periodic reinforcement and cancellation most generally known to musicians is the phenomenon of **beats** produced when tuning.[8] If two tones of the same frequency are played simultaneously, the resultant tone will consist of that frequency with a greater or lesser amplitude, depending upon the degree of phase of the two tones. If one tone is very slightly higher in frequency than the other, beats will be heard as variations in loudness. These beats are the periodic reinforcement and cancellation of two waves due to a difference in frequency. If, for instance, a tone of 150 Hz is played against a tone of 151 Hz, beats at the rate of one-per-second will be heard. If a tone of 440 Hz is played against a tone of 441 Hz, the beat rate will again be one beat per second.

To explain why such a simple tuning mechanism exists in nature, consider a 100 Hz tone and a 101 Hz tone. At the point where 50 cycles have been completed by one instrument, (a half second later) 50.5 cycles have been completed by the other. At the end of one second, 100 cycles have been completed by the first instrument and 101 cycles by the other. There has been a difference of one cycle. Its reinforcement and cancellation has been perceived as one beat or one strengthening and weakening of the amplitude. The greater the difference in frequency, the faster the beats will be. Musicians listen for these beats and then one musician slowly changes pitch until the two tones are "smooth" or altogether free of beats. Problems in smoothing these beats are encountered by young or inexperienced musicians when both try to vary the pitch. Neither has an adequate pitch reference and the beats go away only by "accident." It is important that musicians tune to a stable reference tone.

Beats occur even if the amplitude of the two instruments is not the same. However, the more equal the amplitude of the two instruments, the more noticeable the beats will be.

Perceived Tones

As long as the beats of two instruments happen less than 20 times per second, they will be perceived as beats. If one instrument plays a tone of 256 Hz and another instrument plays a tone of 271 Hz, beats at the rate of 15 per second will occur. If both instruments play relatively loudly, and the instrument producing the 271 Hz tone slowly begins to make its tone sharper (thus widening the difference), at approximately 276 Hz a listener will perceive the combination of the two tones as being quite "rough or raspy." After the rising tone increases to above 276 Hz, the beats will be perceived as a third tone, called a **difference tone** (sometimes called a combination tone).

The beats have reached a frequency that the ear perceives as a separate tone. Interestingly, if a 256 Hz tone and a 286 Hz tone are played simultaneously, it would be difficult for us to discern the 30 Hz difference tone. But, if both instruments start at 256 Hz and one begins to move the pitch upward, the differ-

> **BEATS: The periodic reinforcement and cancellation of two wave fronts with frequencies closer together than 20 Hz.**
>
> **DIFFERENCE TONES: The periodic reinforcement and cancellation of two wave trains with frequencies further apart than 20 Hz may be perceived as a third tone whose frequency is the difference between frequencies of the original tones.**

---

[8] *At least one author has described two kinds of beats: imperfect unisons and mistuned consonances. For further explanation, see: Olsen, op. cit., pp. 258-259.*

ence tone becomes quite distinguishable when the upwardly moving tone passes approximately 276 Hz. This occurs because the difference tone also moves upward in frequency, but at a faster relative rate than the upper tone. It is easier to distinguish a tone sweeping upward in pitch than to perceive a stationary tone that is weaker than the other two. Figure 4-5 shows that the upper tone must be increased in frequency to 512 Hz to slide upward one octave. The difference tone, however, will move up an octave (from 20 Hz to 40 Hz) when the upper tone passes 296 Hz and will increase nearly four octaves as the played tone increases only the one octave.

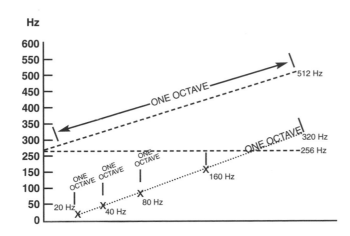

Figure 4-5. The movement of a difference tone.
-------- **Tones that are played.**
················· **Difference tone.**

It is even possible for difference tones to set up what are known as "second order tones" or difference tones created between themselves and one or both of the other tones. This effect is rarely heard outside an electronic music studio. In general, these are not pleasing musical effects, only interesting ones.

If two quite loud tones of low frequency are played simultaneously, it is also possible to hear a tone that is the sum of the two original frequencies. These tones have been labeled **summation tones** and are usually harder to perceive than difference tones. For instance, if one heard two trombones playing, one at 220 Hz and the other at 330 Hz, it would be possible to hear a tone of 550 Hz. Summation tones are most perceptible when their frequencies fall near the mid-range of the audible spectrum.

Difference tones can be explained in terms of beat phenomena, yet summation tones cannot. Consequently, many acousticians and audiologists believe that these summation tones might actually be **subjective tones**, or non-linear responses by parts of the ear. A drum head can serve as a good illustration of a non-linear response. If an instrument is played at close proximity to the head of

> **SUMMATION TONES: Subjective tones produced by the ear that are perceived as the sum of two external frequencies. Summation tones, if heard at all, are heard best when they occur near the middle of the audible frequency spectrum.**
>
> **SUBJECTIVE TONES: Tones that do not exist in the environment, but by forcing parts of the ear into non-linear vibration, are created within the ear itself.**

51

a drum, the head will respond sympathetically and reproduce the tone of the instrument with its full overtone component. If either part of the head is damped or the instrument is played so loudly that the drum head cannot respond accurately (linearly), it will begin to respond by vibrating in parts and not necessarily in harmonic accord with the note being played. The tone or tones produced by the action of the non-linear response of the drum head will have a different fundamental from the original tone and a set of inharmonic overtones.

Some researchers believe that both difference and summation tones may actually be non-linear responses on the part of the eardrum or even other parts of the ear.[9]

There is one more very interesting phenomenon, sometimes called a "residue effect."[10] Clock radios, car radios, transistor radios, ear buds, head phones, and television sets have speakers that may be as small as 2 inches or less in diameter. Rarely are they capable of producing a tone below Middle C on the piano (261.63 Hz), yet we can easily perceive a complete symphony orchestra being reproduced on them, including many notes below Middle C.

Let us consider G below Middle C that has a frequency of 196 Hz. It can be seen that there will be a series of harmonics at 392 Hz, 588 Hz, 784 Hz, 980 Hz, and on up. The difference between any of these overtones is equal to the frequency of the fundamental (See Figure 4-6).

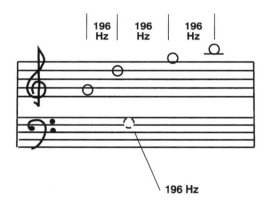

Figure 4-6. A difference tone of 196 Hz produced *in the ear*, as a result of the combined tones of the harmonic series.

When a G of 196 Hz is broadcast and recreated in the 2-inch speaker of a small radio, instead of the fundamental being produced, we hear the harmonics

[9] Backus, John, The Acoustical Foundations of Music, (New York: W. W. Norton & Company, 1969), pp. 105-108.

[10] Schouten, I.F., "Theory of Residue," Proceedings of the Academy of Amsterdam, 43:991 (1940). Winckel, Fritz, Music, Sound & Sensation, translated by Thomas Binkley, (New York: Dover Publications, Inc., 1967), pp. 135-137.

at the above frequencies and our ear supplies the fundamental tone, that is the difference between each adjacent harmonic. For this reason, many people seem quite happy with their small radios and most television sound reproduction.

PRINCIPLES OF GOOD ROOM ACOUSTICS

Information concerning simple and complex waveforms, how instruments produce their characteristic sounds, the effects of the environment, and indeed, the effects of sound itself upon sound have been discussed. All of this information becomes important when deciding upon "ideal" acoustics for a musical rehearsal, a concert setting or even the assembling of a stereo sound system. Since all music is not performed under excellent acoustical conditions, there are some general principles that can make a bad situation better.[11]

Reflection and Reverberation

If a concert is to be given out-of-doors, it would be wise to remember that a hard surface, for instance, near a side of a building, would be a better setting than an open field so that sounds can be reflected back toward the listeners. If the sound source gets somewhat distant from an existing reflective surface, echoes will result. Many so-called "band shells" have been designed so a portion of the rear wall overhangs the performers, thus "catching" those soundwaves traveling upward and reflecting them down again and out toward the audience.

Indoors or out, a certain amount of reflected sound usually enhances the total musical effect. Anyone who has ever played an instrument out-of-doors will have noticed that the sound may have been "dull" or "lifeless." This is because there was little reflected sound to reinforce the primary sound. Indoors, it is quite easy and generally desirable to gain the reinforced complex tone quality that reflected sound can give. Yet this becomes detrimental sometimes. If there are too many reflective surfaces in a room, the effect is that the reflected sound (echoes) becomes mixed with the primary sound, making the music unclear. This effect is known as **reverberation**. In recording studios, parallel walls are avoided in order to allow as little reverberation as possible. In the 21st century, if reverberation is desired, it is created electronically.

Absorption and Insulation

If a room's acoustics are too reflective and the resultant reverberation is annoying, there are a number of possible remedies. Sound **absorption** may be needed. Draperies are an absorbent material for sound. Since the sound is being echoed

---

[11] For a broader understanding of proper room acoustics, see:
Geerdes, H. P., Music Facilities: Building, Equipping and Renovating, *Music Educators National Conference*, 1989, 135p.
Wagner. M.J. & Ostendorf, P., Music Facilities Design Guidelines for Florida's Public Schools, *Office of Educational Facilities, State of Florida, Department of Education, 1940 N. Monroe Street., Tallahassee, FL 32303.*

REVERBERATION: The perceived phenomenon of multiple echoes mixing with the primary sound.

ABSORPTION: The trapping of sound waves in fibrous or porous materials which weakens the wavefront by reflecting and diffusing sound energy.

between hard parallel surfaces, frequently only one wall or part of the wall need be draped. Another absorbing material is carpeting. If draperies or carpeting are not practical, there are a number of good acoustic tiles available. Absorption is the weakening of sound's amplitude. This is accomplished by multiple reflections within the fibers of a fabric or carpet, or by removing a reflective surface and letting the sound travel outward as is the case when one opens doors and windows. In determining the acoustics for a room, it would also be wise to remember that sounds introduced from outside will not be desirable, nor will the transmission of sound from a music room to other nearby rooms.

Probably the least expensive form of sound **insulation** is to make sound pass from one medium to another. When this occurs, much energy is lost. Amplitude can be greatly reduced by this method. This principle of sound insulation can be accomplished in many ways. If a person talks to us while we are swimming, we can no longer hear what the person is saying if we put our ears underwater, because the sound's amplitude is greatly reduced when traveling from air to water. In a house, it is difficult to hear from room to room if doors are shut because the sound energy is greatly reduced when traveling through air, plaster, air, plaster and again air. Yet low-frequency tones may be transmitted or conducted through the floor and beams of the house.

A more expensive but effective method of insulating against sound transmission is to use concrete and other heavy and rigid (not elastic) building materials. Since these building materials do not vibrate very well, they are generally more effective in stopping (damping) sound. Another method is to seal all cracks around doors and windows so that air cannot pass around them. Creating a vacuum is an excellent form of insulation as sound cannot travel in a vacuum. In fact, the windows inside professional recording studios are created from several sealed panes of glass, creating a vacuum between each of them. The individual panes are slightly angled, and may be of different thicknesses, lessening the potential for the sound to reflect and the glass to resonate.

In school music suites and other performing areas, great care must be taken to place enough different materials of varying densities between walls and floors to reduce the transmission of sound to adjacent areas in the buildings. Building materials ought to be heavy and rigid enough to keep most sounds from being transmitted. Further considerations include building walls that go all the way to the floor of the next level, or the roof, if that's what's above the music room; and there should be no shared electrical receptacles between the music room and its neighboring rooms. False ceilings are good transferrers of sound, and shared receptacles create places for sound to diffract.

INSULATION: Preventing sound waves from traveling through physical barriers. This may be accomplished by various combinations of reflection, absorption, diffusion, or by creating a barrier that will not transmit vibration.

DISCUSSION QUESTIONS FOR CHAPTER FOUR

1. What natural environmental forces act to distort or change sound wave fronts?

2. Discuss the eruption of Mt. Krakatoa as an acoustic event.

3. Describe the Doppler phenomenon. Can you think of any practical musical uses?

4. Describe difference tones; summation tones.

5. If a rehearsal hall, made of concrete, has a good deal of echo and reverberation, discuss some practical solutions to solve this problem.

Part II

A review of the anatomy, function and dysfunction of the ear, related neurology, and aural perception is the subject of this section. Much has been written, but little for the musician regarding how we perceive those neurological signals sent to the brain. Yet, musicians and music educators must deal daily with these aural perceptions. It also is extremely important to discuss with musicians and especially music educators, the hazards of prolonged exposure to loud sounds, the kinds and causes of hearing loss, and the treatments available. Hearing and its perception is THE domain of musicians. It would be wise to understand how and why this process works.

Here are some websites that may cast more light on these important matters.

Chapter 5

http://webschoolsolutions.com/patts/systems/ear.htm

http://www.neurophys.wisc.edu/h&b/auditory/animation/animationmain.html

Chapter 6

http://en.wikipedia.org/wiki/Deafness

http://www.nidcd.nih.gov/health/hearing/hearingaid.asp

http://www.who.int/mediacentre/factsheets/fs300/en/index.html

Chapter 7

http://www.cerebromente.org.br/n15/mente/musica.html

http://www.wellcome.ac.uk/News/2001/Features/WTX024041.htm

The Auditory System

CHAPTER 5

Musicians, more than any other group of people, use their sense of audition to make judgments about sound. Most of these judgments require a highly trained and acute sense of **hearing**. Many musicians even attempt to teach these discriminative listening skills to others. If communication of any of these music skills is to happen for enjoyment, for music education or for therapeutic reasons a basic understanding of the hearing process and of hearing problems certainly seems necessary.

HEARING AND PERCEPTION

Hearing is the process by which sounds are transmitted from the environment to our brain. In the environment, sound is physical vibration. Within the depths of the ear, this mechanical energy is changed to electrochemical energy and transmitted to the brain. Hearing is different from **perception**, and a distinction should be made; especially by musicians. One does not perceive vibration, but rather "tone" or "sound." The ear first intensifies the environment's physical vibrations, then changes them to electrochemical energy and sends these messages, via nerve cells, to the brain. The brain translates these auditory signals from electrochemical energy into the sensations that we perceive. While

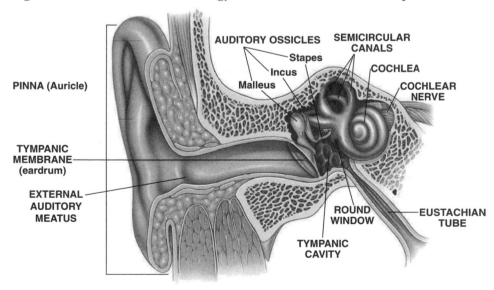

Figure 5-1. The ear.

HEARING: The process by which sounds are transmitted from the environment to our brains.

PERCEPTION: Sensory translations of environmental signals.

we know a good deal concerning how the first links in this chain operate, research is expanding about the process of perception. Brain mapping, PET (positron emission tomography) scans, auditory processing assessments, and auditory evoked potentials are providing more information regarding auditory perception processing. The sensations perceived can be described, but not the process of how electrochemical energy is translated into sensation. The difference between the process of hearing and that of perceiving is important because these are two stages of an essential system for all musicians. This chapter deals with the first stage of that process, hearing.[1]

The ear, our sensory receptor for hearing, is divided into three main parts: the outer, middle and inner ear. Most structures within the ear are important to the processing of sound, but certain parts have other biological functions. The auditory system functions as both a receiver of sound and a mechanism for changing mechanical energy to electrochemical energy.

The outer ear is composed of the **pinna (or auricle)** and the **external auditory meatus** (canal). The middle ear contains three tiny bones called **ossicles** and an opening from the **eustachian tube**. The inner ear consists of the **cochlea**, the **vestibule** and **semicircular canals**, the latter of which functions to control the sense of balance. Some of these main parts of the ear are composed of finer structures. This chapter will be a study of both the main parts and the finer structures of the ear and how they function in the hearing process.[2]

THE OUTER EAR

The outer ear consists of two main parts: the pinna or external ear (sometimes called the auricle), and the meatus (pronounced: me at' us) or external auditory canal. The outer ear ends at the **tympanic membrane** or eardrum. Although it performs other functions as well, the main function of the outer ear is to gather sound from the environment and focus these sound waves toward the eardrum.

The outer ear actually serves four primary functions. First, the long, narrow and tortuous canal protects the more delicate middle and inner ear from foreign bodies by making it inaccessible. Second, it boosts or amplifies high-frequency sounds as the air filled concha and ear canal have a natural resonant frequency. Third, it provides the primary cue for the determination of the elevation of a sound's source. Fourth, the orientation of the pinna assists in distinguishing sounds that arise from in front of the listener from those that arise from behind the listener. This is especially true for high-frequency sounds. [3]

PINNA: The external ear.

EXTERNAL AUDITORY MEATUS: The auditory canal which is approximately one inch in length and terminates at the eardrum.

OSSICLES: The hammer, the anvil and the stirrup; three small bones, each about the size of a grain of rice, which, through lever action, transmit and increase sound pressure as it travels through the middle ear.

EUSTACHIAN TUBE: A tube between the nasopharynx (throat) and the middle ear which keeps air pressure inside the middle ear equalized with that outside.

COCHLEA: The organ of hearing in the inner ear. It's a coiled tube within a tube, which transduces and encodes mechanical vibrations into electro-chemical neurological signals.

VESTIBULE: The area in the base of the cochlea which translates between the semicircular canals and the cochlea.

SEMICIRCULAR CANALS: The semicircular canals, attached to the hearing apparatus, give feedback on one's balance.

TYMPANIC MEMBRANE: The anatomical name for the eardrum.

---

[1] The other process, "perception," will be discussed in Chapter 7.

[2] For a more detailed description of the auditory system: Martin, F.N. & Clark, J.G. (2009) Introduction to Audiology Tenth Edition. Boston, Allyn and Bacon, Pearson Education, Inc.

[3] Bess, F.H., & Humes, L.E. (2008) Audiology The Fundamentals, 4th ed. Philadelphia: Lippincott Williams & Wilkins.

Pinna (Auricle)

The pinna, held upright on the head by cartilage, is composed of folds or convolutions.

Even with the eyes closed, sound sources can be located by detecting very slight delays and differences in the intensity of the sounds. Some of these delays are accomplished by the convolutions of the pinna, whose function is to introduce minute differences in the arrival time of sounds.

Since two ears are used in the normal hearing process, sounds arriving from the environment will differ slightly from one ear to the other and are therefore detected at slightly different times. Those who can use two ears have an advantage, regarding the location of sound sources in the environment, over those who can use only one. However, the greatest advantage of binaural, or **stereophonic hearing** (the use of both ears), is the ability to locate and differentiate sounds from more than one source.[4] Using both ears, sound sources can be heard clearly and located in space even with the eyes closed.

The localization of sound in space is largely a binaural phenomenon. The interaural (between-ear) difference in the time of arrival of the sound is one factor. Interaural time differences are the same for all frequencies. Interaural phase differences vary with frequency. The sound shadow cast by the head (head shadow effect) changes the interaural intensity differences. Interaural time and intensity differences are the strongest acoustic cues for localization.[5]

External Auditory Canal

In some ways the external auditory meatus (canal) is like a closed pipe, open at the pinna and closed at the other end by a semi rigid wall (the tympanic membrane or eardrum). The average length of the ear canal is about 2.5 centimeters, or one inch. In a closed pipe, the air pressure becomes greater at the closed end when pressure variations (sound) are present. These pressure variations move the somewhat elastic tympanic membrane in and out as longitudinal waveforms in correspondence with the vibratory pattern that moves it.

The meatus also keeps the temperature and humidity relatively constant in the canal and keeps the membrane from drying out. The canal secretes a waxy substance called cerumen (sar u' men). We call this substance earwax. Cerumen is antibacterial, and by working its way toward the open end, keeps dirt and dust particles from gathering in the ear canal. In humans and other animals, the canal offers protection to the eardrum. Not all animals have an ear canal or pinna. Birds and reptiles, for instance, have no outer ear. Instead the tympanic membrane is located on the outside of the head.

---

[4] Humes, Larry E., "*Psychoacoustic Foundations of Clinical Audiology,*" *in:* Handbook of Clinical Audiology, Third Edition, *Jack Katz, editor, Williams & Wilkins: Baltimore, 1985, p 110.*

[5] Bess, F.H., & Humes, L.E. (2008) Audiology The Fundamentals, *4th ed. Philadelphia: Lippincott Williams & Wilkins.*

> **STEREOPHONIC HEARING: That portion of the hearing process which deals with the location of sounds in space by the use of our ears.**

THE MIDDLE EAR

The middle ear begins at the boundary formed by the tympanic membrane. Three small bones, the ossicles, each about the size of a grain of rice, perform a kind of lever action that transmits energy from the tympanic membrane to the **oval window** of the inner ear. (To put the ossicles in perspective, they are the smallest bones in the body; the stapes being the smallest of these.) The eustachian tube connects the middle ear to the throat cavity, and thus keeps air pressure inside the middle ear equalized with air pressure outside the head.

The Ossicles

At the eardrum, sound energy is a series of pressure variations. The eardrum changes these pressure variations to mechanical motion and the ossicles transmit this motion to the membrane called the oval window of the inner ear. The three bones (collectively called ossicles) have Latin names: the **malleus**, attached to the tympanic membrane, the **incus** and the **stapes** (sta' peez). Translated into English, they are the hammer, the anvil and the stirrup. They are named for their unique shapes (See Figure 5-2).

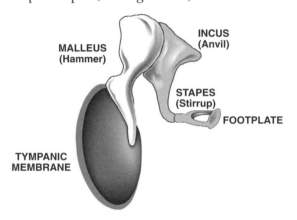

Figure 5-2. The ossicles (middle ear).

These ossicles transmit vibrations from the eardrum to the footplate of the stapes, and by so doing vibrate the oval window that also functions as the entrance to the inner ear. The motion of the largest ossicle, the malleus, becomes an increasingly smaller motion in the incus and finally the stapes, by the simple principle of leverage. As can be seen in Figure 5-3, the lifting end of a lever is forced through a greater distance than the lifted end. This reduced motion is the "cost" paid for the mechanical advantage that allows a heavy load to be moved by only a moderate force.

Since the area at the footplate of the stirrup is smaller than the area of the eardrum, less motion is needed to move the oval window. However, more force is needed. The ossicles give the footplate about eighteen times as much pressure (and reduce proportionately as much motion) as the eardrum. Because the pressure on the oval window is greater than the pressure at the eardrum, and because of the ossicles' leverage on the smaller area, the motion of the stapes' footplate upon the oval window becomes more efficient than eardrum motions.

OVAL WINDOW: The membrane between the footplate of the stapes of the middle ear and the scale vestibuli of the inner ear.

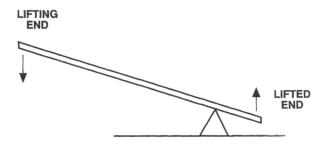

Figure 5-3. A Lever. The lifting end has greater movement but less force; the lifted end has less movement but greater force.

Another important function of the ossicles is to offer some degree of protection to the inner ear from loud noises. This is accomplished in two ways. The ossicles are suspended in space in the middle ear, so they are free to vibrate in all three dimensions. If a loud sound is encountered, the ossicles will move sideways as well as to-and-fro to accommodate the extra energy, thus reducing the extremes of pressure on the oval window. Two small muscles attached to the ossicles also react semi-involuntarily to loud sounds and stiffen the ossicular chain. This process reduces the amount of mechanical motion that is transmitted. Both of these protective devices are limited and neither can react quickly enough to protect against explosive noises or other loud sounds with sudden onsets that take place near the ear.

The Eustachian Tube

The small cavity that contains the ossicles, called the middle ear, is surrounded by bone and filled with air. The middle ear cavity is connected to the oral cavity (throat) by the eustachian tube. The middle ear end of this tube is more "fleshy" and is normally in a collapsed position. Its middle ear end may be slightly opened by yawning, swallowing or the muscular movement of the pinnas! The eustachian tube's function is to equalize the air pressure in the middle ear with that of the air pressure on the outside of the head.

For those who cannot exercise voluntary control over the opening of the eustachian tube, rising rapidly in an elevator or in an airplane occasionally can be a painful experience. As one goes higher, the air pressure outside the head decreases. If the eustachian tube is not opened periodically, the higher air pressure in the middle ear presses outward on both the eardrum and the oval window, resulting in a "stuffy" or "plugged" feeling in the ears.[6] If, on the other hand, one has a cold, the descent of an airplane can cause far greater pain. As one comes from the higher altitudes (an area of reduced air pressure), the greater air pressure on the ground presses in on the tympanic membrane. Similarly, a rapid reduction in air pressure can sometimes result in ruptured eardrums and could conceivably be responsible for damage to the inner ear.

---

[6] *Some people are able to obtain relief by chewing a large amount of gum. The jaw action required for this behavior moves the nasopharyngeal end of the collapsed eustachian tube back and forth, allowing this area to open and thus creating an equalization of air pressure in the middle ear with that of the outside.*

THE INNER EAR

The major components of the inner ear are the cochlea, the vestibule and the semicircular canals. While the cochlea and vestibule are part of the hearing apparatus, the semicircular canals do not normally function as such. Instead, their job is to regulate our sense of balance.

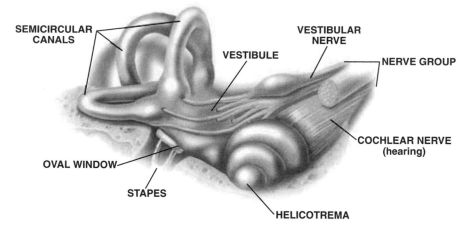

Figure 5-4. The inner ear.

The Vestibular System

The vestibule, as its name describes, is a transitional area between the three semicircular canals and the cochlea. The oval window of the cochlea is located in the inner ear's vestibule. Three semicircular canals, filled with fluid, regulate one's sense of balance. By having one canal in each of the three dimensional planes and in two ears, this system gives constant feedback on one's position in space.

Damage to the semicircular canals or changes in their fluids will result in dizziness, vertigo or lack of balance. An infection or inflammation in one's ear may also cause one or more of these symptoms.

Bone Conduction

Sounds are heard not only through the outer and middle ear, but also through the direct conduction of vibrations through the bones in the head. The clicking of one's teeth and chewing sounds from the mouth may be heard in this way. If a vibrating tuning fork is placed on the forehead, mastoid, or even the teeth, some of the vibrations are conducted directly to the cochlea of the inner ear. This kind of conductive hearing is very important when trying to determine whether a person has a hearing loss in the middle ear or has sensorineural damage in the inner ear. If a person has experienced a hearing loss and can hear a bone oscillator or tuning fork placed on the mastoid or forehead, the hearing loss has probably occurred in the outer or middle ear. If the bone oscillator or tuning fork cannot be heard well using this method, the hearing loss is probably located in the inner ear. This traditional test of bone conductivity will be discussed in more detail in Chapter 6.

The Anatomy of the Cochlea

The cochlea (Latin for snail) is generally considered to be the true organ of hearing. It is coiled approximately 2 3/4 turns, yet the spiral shape itself seems to serve no purpose in the process of hearing other than that of a biological space saver.[7] The cochlea is surrounded by bone. Inside, it is a tube within a tube. If the cochlea could be unrolled and sliced lengthwise in half, it would look something like Figure 5-5. Its cross section appears as in Figure 5-6.

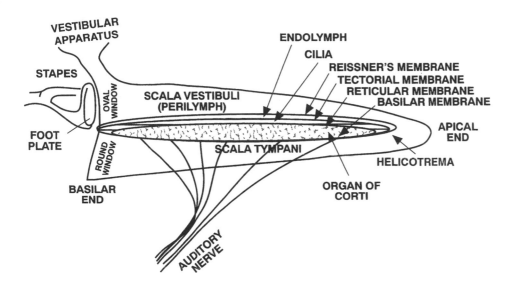

Figure 5-5. Diagram of the Unrolled Cochlea.

In many ways, the cochlea is a most remarkable organ. It acts as a most efficient **transducer**, i.e., a converter of mechanical to electrochemical energy. It is important to know the parts of the cochlea so you can understand how mechanical energy (vibration) is transduced to electrochemical energy within the cochlea, and how those signals are sent to the brain.

Behind the oval window, located at the base of the cochlea (large end), is a tube filled with fluid called **perilymph**. This tube runs the full length of the cochlea to the **apical end** (small end), turns and comes back the full length again to the **round window**, that is a membrane stretched over the remaining portion of the cochlear base. It also mediates with the middle ear. The top tube is called the **scala vestibuli**, the area where the tube turns back on itself is called the **helicotrema** (heli-co-tre'-ma) and the bottom portion of the tube is called the **scala tympani**.

Through the center of the cochlea runs another enclosed tube known as the **cochlear duct**, filled with another fluid called **endolymph**. The cochlear duct is separated from the scala vestibuli by Reissner's membrane. Along the lower side

---

[7] *The coiled shape requires less area than would a hypothetical, unrolled cochlea.*

TRANSDUCER: An apparatus that converts one form of energy into another form; in this case mechanical energy (vibration) into electrochemical signals. Another good example of a transducer is the speaking unit (microphone) in the telephone.

PERILYMPH: A seawater-like fluid in the scala vestibuli, helicotrema and scala tympani of the cochlea.

APICAL END: From the Latin "apex" meaning tip or end. In the cochlea, the small end in the center of the coil. The opposite end from the cochlear base.

ROUND WINDOW: The membrane separating the middle ear cavity from the scala tympani of the inner ear. The membrane is flexible and will be in opposite phase with the oval window when a tonal stimulus is present.

SCALA VESTIBULI: The upper level of the cochlea bordered by the oval window at its inception, the helicotrema at the apex, the cochlear wall, and Reissner's membrane. The scala vestibuli is filled with perilymph.

HELICOTREMA: A narrow opening at the apical end of the cochlea joining the scala vestibuli from the scala tympani.

SCALA TYMPANI: The lower level of the cochlea bordered by the helicotrema at the apical end, the round window at the base, the cochlear wall and the basilar membrane. The scala tympani is filled with perilymph.

COCHLEAR DUCT: A tube within a tube lying between the scala vestibuli and the scala tympani. It contains endolymph and houses the Organ of Corti. Along its lower wall is the basilar membrane. Its upper wall is Reissner's membrane.

ENDOLYMPH: The fluid in the cochlear duct.

of the cochlear duct runs the **organ of Corti**,[8] supported by the **basilar membrane**. The very important organ of Corti is composed of approximately 23,500 inner and outer hair cells, each of which project about fourteen **cilia** up into the endolymph through the **reticular membrane**. Just above the hair cells is another membrane called the **tectorial membrane**.

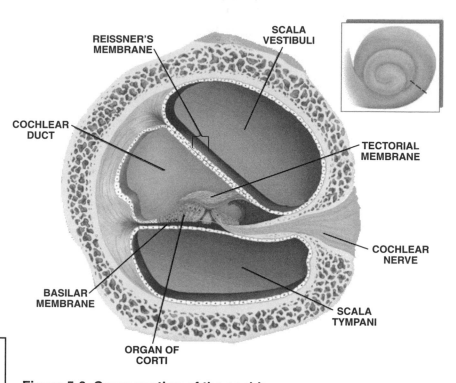

Figure 5-6. Cross section of the cochlea.

ORGAN OF CORTI: The organ which contains about 23,500 hair cells. Corti's organ is supported by the basilar membrane which, when deformed by pressure, stimulates the hair cells to trigger nerve impulses.

BASILAR MEMBRANE: The membrane which divides the scala tympani from the cochlear duct. It is this membrane which supports the organ of Corti.

CILIA: The microscopic "hairs" of the hair cells extending through the reticular membrane. There are approximately fourteen cilia atop each hair cell.

RETICULAR MEMBRANE: The membrane covering the hair cells, yet allowing the cilia to extend upward through it.

TECTORIAL MEMBRANE: A membrane extending across the top of Corti's organ. When the cilia are deformed by being compressed against this membrane, the hair cells stimulate the auditory nerve to "fire."

In 1978, David Kemp published what is now a classic paper[9] demonstrating that the ear was capable of producing, as well as receiving, sounds. These sounds are produced by the sensory cells in the cochlear and are called "evoked otoacoustic emissions," or OAE. The ability of the outer hair cells to contract and elongate in response to sound stimulation results in the amplification of the mechanical response in the inner ear (basilar membrane) at low sound intensities. It is believed that the trigger initiating a series of electrical and chemical processes within the hair cells is the shearing and displacement force of the outer hair cells between the tectorial membrane and the basilar membrane. [10]

---

[8] *Named after its discoverer, Alfonso Corti, who first described this structure in 1851.*

[9] *Kemp D.T. Stimulated acoustic emissions from within the human auditory system.* Journal Acoustical Society of America *64: 1386-1391, 1978*

[10] *Hall, J.W. & Mueller, H.G. (1997)* Audiologists' Desk Reference Volume 1. *San Diego: Singular Publishing Group, Inc.*

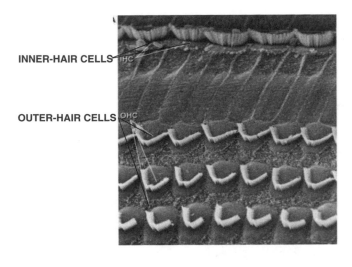

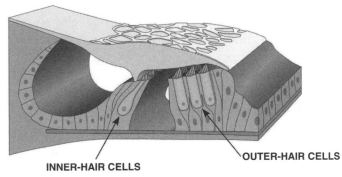

Figure 5-7. Microanatomy of the organ of Corti.

An understanding of the anatomy of the cochlea is crucial to the understanding of its function. It is particularly important that the above text be read and reread in conjunction with the study of Figures 5-5 – 5-7.

Cochlear Function

As the footplate of the stapes presses against the oval window, perilymph is displaced and pressure waves are formed. If the displacement happens very slowly (slower than sound waves), as with changes in air pressure, the compression wave in the perilymph travels the full length of the tube, through the scala vestibuli, around the opening in the apical end (the helicotrema), back through the scala tympani, and presses the round window, that moves outward to accommodate the pressure exerted by the perilymph.

Because sound waves are not slow, the perilymph does not have time to let the pressure travel the long way around. A hydraulic pressure wave is formed in the perilymph at a point determined by the frequency of the sound source. The cochlear duct is deformed at this point along its length, and it bends and bulges down into the scala tympani where the tectorial membrane, hair cells, reticular membrane, organ of Corti, and the basilar membrane are, in turn, deformed with respect to each other. This sliding or shearing action generates an electrochemical charge that stimulates auditory nerve fibers to fire impulses as the cilia are deformed or compressed. The exact method by which this mechanical energy is transduced (converted to electrochemical energy) has been the subject of a neurological quest for several centuries.[11]

Cochlear Microphonics

Because all matter is electrical in nature, certain events can cause an electrical potential called voltage to be established. This potential, in turn, can cause an electric current to flow. When vibrations of a tone are introduced into the ear, an electrical potential can be observed at the round window of the cochlea. The changes in this potential follow those of the motions of the stapes footplate. Because this transducing action follows quite closely the way a microphone works, the name "microphonic" has been given to this phenomenon.[12] Cochlear microphonic action apparently arises from electrochemical reactions involving the hair cells and cilia of the organ of Corti. When microscopic electrodes are inserted into the scala tympani, the electrochemical reactions seem to mirror the motions of the basilar membrane at particular localized areas along its length. Because of this, the built in "microphonic" has been a useful tool for studying exactly how mechanical energy is transduced. [13]

The Coding of Auditory Signals

The frequency of a particular sound seems to determine where along the basilar membrane maximum physical displacement occurs. The apical end is most displaced by low frequencies while the basal end (base) is maximally displaced by high tones (See Figure 5-8). Thus the hair cells and their cilia located along the organ of Corti are differentially stimulated by tones of different frequencies. Frequency then, is coded by the particular area along the basilar membrane that is maximally displaced.

In the 20 Hz through 60 Hz range, the displacement of the basilar membrane occurs as a whole and produces, in the auditory nerve, signals that are the same as the frequency of the sound. At about 60 Hz, the basilar membrane begins to vibrate unequally over its length, with each frequency producing a maximum displacement at a slightly different location along the membrane. At frequencies of about 4000 Hz, pitch seems to be determined primarily by the location of maximum vibratory amplitude (point of greatest displacement) along the basilar membrane. This theory is known as the "Place Theory" of hearing. [14]

---

[11] *"Thus in the sixth chapter I have been able to make use of the new physiological and anatomical researches on the ear. This has led to a modification of my view of the action of Corti's arches ...." Herman L.F. Helmholtz, preface to the third German edition,* On the Sensations of Tone, *May, 1870.*

[12] *First reported: Wever, E.G. & Bray, C.W., Proceedings of the National Academy of Science (Washington, D.C., (1930) 16: 344-350.*

[13] *Berlin, C.I. & Hood, L.J, Current Physiologic Bases of Audiologic Interpretation and Management in Handbook of Clinical Audiology, 6th Edition (2009). Katz, J., (Editor in Chief). Medwetsky, L., Burkard, R., Hood, L J. (Eds) Philadelphia: Lippincott Williams & Wilkins.*

[14] *von Bekesy, Georg, Experiments in Hearing, E. G. Wever, Ed., (New York: McGraw-Hill Book Company, 1960).*

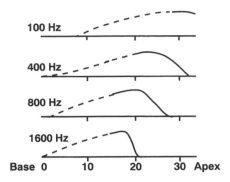

Figure 5-8. Displacement patterns of the basilar membrane as it reacts to different stimulus frequencies.

Detecting loudness seems to be a result of how many hair cells are displaced. The more intense a tone, the greater the pressure, and consequently the more the peripheral displacement of hair cells and the more auditory nerves that fire. Also, as sound intensity increases and the pressure on the basilar membrane becomes greater, the rate of firing increases. When very high intensities are encountered, the "rest time" between firings decreases—allowing more firings within a given time. Without the necessary refractory time the auditory system becomes "fatigued" and it progressively responds more and more poorly to incoming signals. Prolonged exposure to intense stimuli can cause acute auditory fatigue and a consequent temporary hearing loss. Repeated exposures to intense sounds result in permanent damage to these nerves. (Musicians: Please re-read, and heed, the previous sentence.)

The Place Theory of cochlear action is a relatively new explanation for how auditory signals are coded. In the middle of the nineteenth century, the German physiologist and physicist Herman von Helmholtz theorized that cells within the basilar membrane were each under tension and "tuned" to particular frequencies along the basilar membrane. He described these transverse fibers as "strings" that correspondingly vibrated according to the fundamental and overtones of a sound along the basilar membrane. For many years, this "Resonance Place" theory was judged to be a proper description of the inner ear's function. In fact, in some circles the "Place" portion of the Helmholtz theory still stands.

In the late nineteenth century (1886), William Rutherford, an English physiologist, presented his "Telephone" theory. He described the function of the cochlea as a transducer, an instrument just like a telephone that transduces mechanical vibration to electrical energy for transmission over wires. According to this theory, every hair cell would respond to every tone, thus translating sound into electrical "vibrations." While this theory is no longer thought to be tenable, the concept of auditory "coding" along the auditory nerve has survived.

As recently as 1961, Georg von Békésy, a Hungarian scientist working at Harvard University, received the Nobel Prize for establishing the present Place Theory of cochlear action. His research included building mechanical models of the inner ear that were used in studying the action of the fluids of the cochlea, and he miniaturized surgical tools to remove the cochlea from human cadavers for study. His work illustrates that standing hydraulic (fluid) waves are formed in the perilymph by tones of various frequencies that press upon and deform areas along the basilar membrane. Subsequent study of subjects who were deaf to only certain frequencies has shown localized degeneration in the cochlea at areas corresponding to Bekesy's findings.

There are still many questions to be answered regarding the cochlea's electrochemical activity.[15] Cochlear microphonics, for example, is still the subject of intensive research. A further explanation of nerve cell firing is addressed in Chapter 7 concerning aural perception.

In summary, we "hear" with our brain, not our ears. As will be seen in Chapter 7, the auditory cortex processes sound at different levels.

DISCUSSION QUESTIONS FOR CHAPTER FIVE

1. Of what "practical" use is the outer ear?

2. How is the intensity of a tonal stimulus increased in the middle ear?

3. Describe the process by which extremely loud sounds reduce hearing acuity. In what frequency range does this most often occur? (see Chapter 6, "Noise," as well.)

4. Describe the process by which mechanical vibration is encoded into neurological signals.

5. How are frequency and amplitude each encoded neurologically?

---

[15] *In Katz, J., (Editor in Chief). Medwetsky, L., Burkard, R., Hood, L J. (Eds) (2009) Handbook of Clinical Audiology, 6th Edition. Philadelphia: Lippincott Williams & Wilkins.*

Hearing Loss & Deafness

CHAPTER 6

THE RANGE OF AUDITORY IMPAIRMENT

As musicians and music teachers, we can readily appreciate that early recognition of hearing loss in ourselves or in others can save many years of aggravation in struggling to accomplish aural tasks physically beyond the capability of the hearing apparatus. Just the recognition of a hearing problem can sometimes be a comfort, and diagnosis can often lead to medical or surgical treatment that will improve hearing.

Deafness is the word most commonly used to describe total hearing loss.[1] Many descriptors have been used to denote a partial hearing loss; hard of hearing and hearing impaired are common terms. Other terms describe particular types of hearing impairment. There is a continuum of hearing loss that runs from very minor auditory acuity problems all the way to bilateral total deafness. The measurement of auditory acuity has been fairly well standardized.

Hearing loss or deafness can be the result of many things. Disease in any portion of the ear can result in hearing loss. Other causes of hearing loss include the side effects of taking of certain drugs, exposure to loud sounds or noises, heredity, birth defects, and the normal process of aging. Diseases and other high risk factors incurred by a mother while pregnant can also cause hearing loss in the child. Even if one has a hearing loss, aggravation or further damage may occur under certain circumstances. In this chapter, discussion will be confined to the more common causes of hearing loss and deafness. Medical and surgical treatments for hearing problems will also be discussed where appropriate, in order to facilitate discussions about these problems between the reader and qualified health professionals. For losses of hearing that are not surgically correctable, it will be beneficial to locate audiologic (or aural) rehabilitation programs so that one can learn to conserve what hearing ability remains, and in cases where hearing impairment is profound, learn how to better communicate with those affected.

Otolaryngology is the branch of medicine that specializes in the diagnosis and treatment of ear, nose, throat, and head and neck disorders. A commonly used term for this specialty is ENT (ear, nose and throat). **Audiologists** are the

---

DEAFNESS: Total hearing loss.

OTOLARYNGOLOGY: Medical specialty associated with diagnosis and management of diseases of the ear, nose, and throat and related structures of the head and neck.

AUDIOLOGIST: A primary health care professional who evaluates, treats, and manages hearing loss and balance disorders in adults and children.

---

[1] Ginsberg, I.A., & White, T.P., "Otologic Considerations in Audiology," in: Handbook of Clinical Audiology, *Jack Katz, editor, Williams & Wilkins: Baltimore, 1985, pp 15–38.*

primary health care professionals who evaluate, diagnose, treat, and manage hearing loss and balance disorders in adults and children.

Hearing impairments can be categorized into three types: poor conduction of sound to the cochlea, some form of abnormality of the cochlea, and dysfunction of the central nervous system. With today's technology hearing loss can be further classified into eight types of hearing loss **Conductive, Mixed, Sensory, Neural, Sensorineural Hearing Loss,** Brainstem, Cortical, and Pseudohypacusis.[2] The causes or etiology of the most common types of hearing loss are discussed below. Pseudohypacusis or functional hearing loss is an exaggeration or feigned hearing loss. The other types of hearing losses refer to where in the anatomy the hearing loss occurs or site of lesion of the loss.

Conductive Hearing Loss

The causes and treatment of conductive hearing loss are important to this discussion because by knowing more about such problems, conservation of hearing can result. In both the outer and middle ears the conduction of sound is mechanical. Blockage of sound vibrations (damping) by any means will reduce hearing acuity. If a loss of hearing is due to a blockage in the meatus or an impairment of the ossicles, it can usually be corrected. Even a ruptured or perforated eardrum will generally heal or can be surgically corrected with little or no residual loss in hearing. A tympanic membrane may even be surgically patched or replaced.

An audiologist should be consulted, and an **audiometric examination** given if a hearing loss is suspected.[3] A battery of tests is used to determine the location or site of lesion of a hearing impairment. One standard evaluation employs air and bone conduction pure tones as stimuli.[4] To determine if the loss is conductive or sensorineural, the results from the air and bone conduction are compared. If the person hears the sound normally by bone conduction, it can be assumed that the hearing loss is probably not due to sensorineural damage. However, if bone conducted sound is reduced (or not heard at all) a sensorineural hearing loss may be suspected. There are some cases where this may not necessarily be true. Some skulls do not conduct vibrations as well as others. A fixated footplate of the stapes upon the oval window of the cochlea can also reduce, to some extent, bone conducted sound. The perceived frequency of the stimulus may also be affected. If bone conduction is reduced but there is still an "air/bone gap" (bone is still better than air), then the loss is a mixed hearing loss including conductive and sensorineural components.

CONDUCTIVE HEARING LOSS: A shift of the threshold of audibility due to mechanical impairment of any part or combination of parts of the ear.

MIXED HEARING LOSS: Hearing loss that includes both conductive and sensorineural impairments.

SENSORY HEARING LOSS: Hearing loss from pathology involving the sensory end organ in the cochlea. Most common sites include outer and inner hair cells within the Organ of Corti.

NEURAL HEARING LOSS: Hearing loss from pathology to the auditory branch of the Cranial Nerve VIII (8th nerve).

SENSORINEURAL HEARING LOSS: Noncorrectable hearing loss due to damage, malformation or degeneration of a portion of the neural system in the ear.

AUDIOMETRIC EXAMINATION: A general name given to hearing tests which include the charting of minimum threshold intensity, rating of a wide frequency range in both ears, word perception, bone conduction and a visual inspection of the external ear. Audiometric tests are usually given in a sound-treated chamber and take from one-half hour to three hours, depending upon the number and types of tests given.

[2] *Department of Veterans Affairs staff at Mountain Home, TN, Long Beach, CA, Nashville, TN. The Audiology Primer for Students and Health Care Professionals, 3rd edition. Retrieved May 14, 2009, from East Tennessee State University Web site: http://etsu.edu/crhs/commdis/audiology/audiologyebook.aspx*

[3] *What is an Audiologist? Retrieved May 14, 2009 from American Academy of Audiology Web site: http://www.audiology.org.*

[4] *Bess, F.H., & Humes, L.E. (2008) Audiology The Fundamentals, 4th ed. Philadelphia: Lippincott Williams & Wilkins.*

Although a separate test battery to assess the status of the middle ear has been available since the 1970s, continued research refines the information we obtain. The most common test of the Immittance Test Battery is tympanometry that measures the mobility of the middle ear when air pressure in the external ear canal is varied. This test battery in conjunction with pure tone testing helps identify where the hearing loss (site of lesion) occurs. It also helps assess eustachian tube dysfunction.

Some of the more common causes of conductive hearing loss occurring in the outer and middle ear, and their treatments, are described in the following sections.

The Outer Ear

The natural secretion of cerumen in the external auditory canal helps keep the canal's tissues soft and traps foreign particles that enter. Normally, it works its way forward and out of the opening, bit by bit. The constant insertion of mini earphones (ear buds), hearing aids, hairpins, match sticks, cotton swabs, paper clips and even more foolish objects can cause the cerumen to become impacted against or near the eardrum, thus effectively damping vibration of the eardrum by restricting entering vibrations. Physicians or other trained professionals can evaluate and appropriately remove cerumen usually by one of three methods: curetting (literally, "scraping") the cerumen, irrigation of the meatus, or suctioning. It's always wise to ask your physician if you are a candidate for over-the-counter drops, and what method would be appropriate for your individual needs.

There are other, less frequent causes of hearing loss that can occur in the outer ear. Malformations of the meatus by birth defect or from injuries can cause a conductive hearing loss. These defects are sometimes surgically correctable. **External otitis** (inflammation of the ear canal) can cause a noticeable hearing loss due to a swelling of the tissues of the meatus. It is important to keep water out of the ear canal when it becomes infected. Because water softens the skin, it tends to spread the infection. External otitis is often very painful. The layman's term is often called "swimmer's ear." It is also possible that old perforations of the tympanic membrane may have formed scar tissue that is thicker than normal. In effect, scar tissue can do to the eardrum what a drum head with uneven thickness does to a drum's sound. It results in uneven and unnatural sound production and proportionately poorer sound conduction.

The Middle Ear

The middle ear is susceptible to several problems that can lead to conductive hearing loss.

(1) Cysts, tumors, or growths may form that inhibit the movement of the ossicles.
(2) **Otitis media** may cause hearing loss.
(3) Bony deposits may be formed near the footplate of the stapes, thus inhibiting its action upon the oval window (called **otosclerosis**).
(4) An interruption of the ossicles.

EXTERNAL OTITIS: Otitis (O ti' tis) means inflammation of the ear. External refers to the outer ear.

OTITIS MEDIA: Inflammation in the middle ear.

OTOSCLEROSIS (O' to skler o' sis): A disease in which bony growths inhibit the mechanical operation of the parts of the middle ear.

All of the above problems may occur in one or both ears. As would be expected, an abnormal tissue growth or swelling within the confines of the middle ear can cause pressure and consequently a damping action on the ossicles. Hearing loss from the growth of a cyst is likely to develop slowly over time, and is not likely to be noticed immediately. Medical or surgical treatment for a middle ear cyst is usually completely successful.

People who travel in aircraft or dive beneath the sea experience rather rapid changes in air pressure and are therefore more susceptible to the problem of differential pressure in the middle ear. When one moves from areas of low air pressure to areas of greater pressure, care must be taken. If the eustachian tube is not opened periodically to equalize the air pressure, the pressure in the middle ear becomes either less than, or greater than that of the outside thus creating either a partial vacuum or pressure in the middle ear. Yawning, swallowing, chewing gum, drinking a liquid, moving the muscles that control the ears or just moving the jaws will usually open the eustachian tubes. Many who have trouble equalizing the pressure by these means experience pain. Furthermore, extreme pressure differences may result in the dislodging (disarticulation) of the ossicles. Liquid from the capillaries (small blood vessels) may literally be pulled through the capillary walls into the middle ear, thus helping to reduce pressure differences. This, however, fills the middle ear with fluid and thus inhibits the action of the ossicles. The drainage of the resultant fluid through a surgical incision (myringotomy) made in the tympanic membrane may be necessary.

It is also possible for bacteria to be introduced into the middle ear through the eustachian tube, especially when one has a cold or a throat infection. If bacteria do make their way into the middle ear and an infection results, it should be treated immediately. Middle ear infections may respond well to antibiotics. Infections can cause pus and other fluids to fill the middle ear cavity—that lies close to the brain. A sharp blow to the head could conceivably cause a small break in the skull, from which the infection might be introduced into the brain cavity. This kind of middle ear infection is usually accompanied by quite a lot of pain, and sometimes a disturbed sense of balance, that may be due to concomitant inflammation of the semi-circular canals. Medical attention should be sought immediately if middle ear infection is suspected. Persons with autoimmune diseases, including AIDS, often have hearing loss due to middle ear disorders. Also, radiation in the head and neck area can result in middle ear disorders.

Otosclerosis is a bone disease that may begin in youngsters and progress gradually, but usually occurs at a later age, in the 50s and 60s. Females have a higher incidence of otosclerosis. The bone that surrounds the middle ear is invaded by softer bone tissue that gradually hardens. In some cases it fixes the footplate of the stapes to the oval window so that conduction of sound vibration is impaired. This disease is hereditary and is much more prevalent in Caucasians than in other races. Often these growths do not inhibit hearing for many years, if at all. It is sometimes surgically correctable, and the operation is performed under a microscope with special microsurgical instruments. The stapes is removed and replaced by a prosthesis. This operation has been judged suitable to recover hearing loss to the degree that everyday speech can again become recognizable and audible without the use of a hearing aid. Sometimes, instead of the bony growth occurring around the stapes footplate and oval window, it will gradually cover the round window and inhibit its elasticity. If this happens the perilymph is no longer free to conduct the activity of the oval window's pressure. Persons with otosclerosis need to be diligent with the use of ear protection because the middle ear muscle cannot move a fixed stapes to protect against loud noises.

Although the primary treatment of a conductive hearing loss is medical intervention, there are times, if cleared by a physician, that hearing aids provide a very clear signal as amplification replaces the mechanical advantage of the middle ear. The amplified sounds are then provided to a normal neural auditory pathway.

The Inner Ear

All inner ear dysfunctions are not the result of sensorineural damage as had been previously thought. Meniere's disease, characterized by the sudden onset of vertigo (dizziness), fluctuating hearing loss, **tinnitus**, and a report of fullness in the ears, has sometimes been found to be amenable to medical treatment.

SENSORINEURAL HEARING LOSS

In only some cases can surgery be relied upon to alleviate sensorineural hearing loss. If hearing loss results from pressure exerted by a tumorous growth upon the auditory nerve, the blood supply to the nerve, or even upon the basilar membrane, surgical removal of the tumor or growth is possible. In some cases this operation is not undertaken to repair hearing loss but rather to prevent other symptoms or to save a life. Pressure upon these areas might indicate the development of further pressure that may starve neurons in the brain stem and can, in some cases, cause death. Nerve cells will not regenerate. Therefore, if neurons are destroyed, the function they provide can no longer be accomplished.

Aging (Presbycusis)

The process of aging is the largest single cause of sensorineural hearing loss. As we grow older, the ossicles may become somewhat more rigid, and the tissues of the tympanic membrane, oval and round windows more brittle and less flexible. Also, neurons along the basilar membrane may die due to overexposure to noises encountered through life or from lack of adequate blood supply. That is often a condition of aging. Neurons in the central nervous system may also die and degenerate due to lack of adequate blood supply. These aging effects happen slowly over a period of years. They also happen earlier in some people than in others. Since we hear with our brains, there are problems with the aging brain that are mixed with the problems of the auditory system.

> **TINNITUS (Tin i' tus): The medical term for the perception of sound in one or both ears or in the head when no external sound is present.**

Drugs

A great deal of controversy and speculation has been noted over the use of certain drugs and antihistamines (drugs used to treat allergies). Certain chemical treatments for other ailments have been linked with sensorineural hearing loss. The use of quinine and the use of aspirin may result in some sensorineural damage in sensitive people. Even excessive use of tobacco, caffeine in coffee, tea, or chocolate is thought by some physicians to increase tinnitus and reduce blood flow to the inner ear. A number of other drugs (ototoxic drugs) have been linked with hearing loss, and their names and hazards are well known to medical professionals. Some are used in chemotherapy treatments. Only in extreme instances (to save lives), are these ototoxic drugs administered.

Noise

It cannot be stated too often that loud sounds and noises can cause hearing loss.[5] Hearing loss may be temporary, such as after working in or visiting a factory, a rifle range, etc. Usually after long exposure, voices seem muffled and the ears ring. After a few hours, overnight, or sometimes as long as a week, hearing returns to normal. In factories where noisy environments prevail, as in portions of the aircraft industry, it is mandatory that workers wear "hearing protectors." These may be either earplugs or headphone like protectors or both, depending upon the decibel level of the work environment.

The temporary inability to perceive sounds at very low loudness levels is referred to as a **temporary threshold shift**. Interestingly, the shift is greatest approximately one half octave above where the noise exposure was greatest. When hearing returns to normal sensitivity, it does so last in the 3000 to 5000 Hz range. Most noise related temporary hearing loss is partial (as opposed to total), and there is usually a loss of sensitivity to high tones. Because the human ear reacts so differently to diverse kinds of noise exposure and because there is so much variability in individual hearing ability, any numbers used to describe these hearing losses are not very helpful. It is known that noises that are so loud as to cause pain will most certainly eventually cause hearing loss if exposure continues.

Pain, however, does not always accompany hearing loss. Herein lies the danger. Repeated and prolonged exposure to loud noise may raise one's pain threshold while not reducing the susceptibility to sensorineural damage (See Figure 6-1). Permanent sensorineural damage may result from prolonged or repeated exposure to loud noise, or from a blow to the ear that conducts a violently percussive wave through the outer, middle and inner ear. A very loud cannon shot or nearby explosion can cause the same problem. Sometimes in extreme cases of noise exposure, the eardrum is ruptured and minor bleeding can result. Interestingly, the likelihood of permanent sensorineural damage seems to be greater if the eardrum does not rupture at the onset of an extremely loud sound, thereby indicating another safety feature of our hearing apparatus.

> **TEMPORARY THRESHOLD SHIFT:** Temporary hearing loss that is due to exposure to loud noises. Sometimes called "Acoustic Trauma."

---

[5] Chasin, M. (1996) Musicians and the Prevention of Hearing Loss, *San Diego: Singular Publishing.*

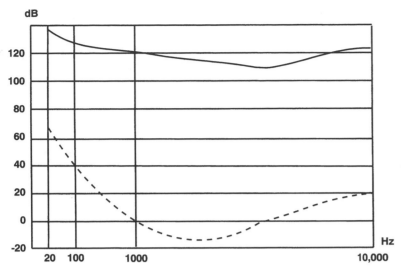

Figure 6-1.
.........Minimum intensity threshold (average)
_____Pain threshold (average)

Noise-induced hearing loss depends on several factors, including the acoustic characteristics of the sound: intensity, duration, and frequency content; the length of exposure, and the susceptibility of the person. Measurements of the sound pressure of the sound linked to the length of time exposed compose the *Damage Risk Criteria* developed by the Occupational Safety and Health Administration. Sounds can be recreational and/or pleasant—like music, but still toxic to one's ears. Portable music players allowing us to listen to music for long, uninterrupted periods, are a subject of continued contemporary research. Limiting the use of high volume settings and the length of listening each day is the best way to minimize risk of permanent, noise-induced hearing loss.[6]

Tinnitus

Tinnitus has two correct pronunciations: tin-NIGHT-us or TIN-it-us. It is the medical term for the perception of sound in one or both ears or in the head when no external sound is present. It is often referred to as "ringing in the ears," although some people hear hissing, roaring, whistling, chirping, or clicking. Tinnitus can be intermittent or constant—with single or multiple tones—and its perceived volume can range from subtle to shattering. The exact physiological cause or causes of tinnitus are not known. There are, however, several likely sources, all of which are known to trigger or worsen tinnitus. Some of these have been listed earlier in this chapter in the section, "Drugs."

The American Tinnitus Association[7] estimates that over 50 million Americans experience tinnitus to some degree. Of these, about 12 million have severe enough tinnitus to seek medical attention. And about two million patients are so seriously debilitated that they cannot function on a "normal," day-to-day basis.

---

[6] *Bess, F.H., & Humes, L.E. (2008)* Audiology The Fundamentals, *4th ed. Philadelphia: Lippincott Williams & Wilkins.*

[7] *FAQ. Retrieved June 8, 2009 from American Tinnitus Association Web site:* http://www.ata.org/

Interestingly, one of the newer treatments for tinnitus, often caused by noise induced hearing loss, involves wearing a device that customizes acoustic stimuli embedded in spectrally modified and designed relaxing music, that is delivered at a comfortable listening level. Research is ongoing for the treatment of tinnitus.

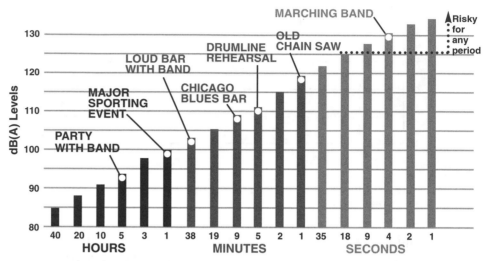

© Copyright Etymotic Research, Inc. Used with permission.

Figure 6-2. Allowable Daily Exposure (OSHA and NIOSH)

Source level in dB	85	88	90	92	94	95	97	100	105	110	115	120
OSHA (hrs)	16		8	6		4	3	2	1	1/2	1/4	1/8
NIOSH (hrs)	8	4			1	3/4	1/2	1/4				

OSHA (Occupational Safety and Health Association) and NIOSH (National Institute for Occupational Safety and Health) values listed above are given in daily exposure limits. According to the OSHA standard, a person can be exposed to a 95 dB environment for 4 hours before risking hearing damage. With 10 dB of protection that person can be exposed to 95 dB for 16 hours per day. NIOSH values are more conservative. For maximum protection, foam earplugs, muffs or other hearing protection devices are recommended.

© Copyright Etymotic Research, Inc. Used with permission.

Figure 6-3. Allowable Sound Exposure To Be Safe.

Non-Organic Hearing Loss

There may be psychological explanations for certain cases of hearing impairment. Some terms commonly used for nonorganic hearing loss are **pseudohypoacusis**, functional hearing loss, and psychogenic or hysterical deafness. With the complete battery of test it can be determine if there is an organic cause to the hearing loss; but nonorganic causes may vary and they are not always clearly understood.

> **PSEUDOHYPOACUSIS: Hearing loss that is feigned or exaggerated.**

Assessment of Hearing Loss for Brainstem and Cortical Hearing Losses

A battery of audiological and medical tests is used in diagnosing these hearing losses. Magnetic Resonance Imaging (MRI) and Computed Tomagraphy (CT) may be part of the test battery. Causes can be from vascular accidents or strokes, space occupying masses (including acoustic neuroma or tumor), traumatic brain injury (TBI), infection, and from demyelinating disease such as Multiple Sclerosis. Head trauma resulting in Traumatic Brain Injury (TBI) can range from a sudden hearing loss to auditory processing disorders. These TBI's can be the result of explosions, from war injuries, motorcycle accidents, or other extreme events.

Auditory Processing Tests focus on how the two ears work together in understanding speech, processing speech in background noise, filtered speech, and compressed speech. See Chapter 7 for more information on Perception of Sound. It may be helpful for listeners with Auditory Processing Disorders (APD) to be provided verbal instructions without music or other auditory distractions in the background.

The advent of **Evoked Potential** assessments including Auditory Brainstem Response (ABR) testing allows more specific site of lesion diagnosis with non-invasive procedures. ABR is a summed response of many single nerve fibers firing synchronously in response to acoustic signals and can be performed while the patient is asleep. These responses may be correlated to hearing ability, which is why it is one of the "gold" standard assessments for testing babies as well as difficult to test patients. ABR provides information on the integrity of the brainstem to auditory stimuli. ABR also helps us separate neural loss from sensory loss assessed with Otoacoustic Emissions (OAEs) that are echoes from the outer hair cells in the cochlea.

The separation of the loss of hearing from disorders such as Auditory Processing Disorders (APD) and Auditory Neuropathy/Auditory Dys-Synchrony (AN/AD) determines if distortion of sound or the ability to separate speech from noise is the major difficulty. More research is still needed regarding persons with these auditory disorders and the affect of distortion and timing for music.

CONSERVATION OF HEARING

The conservation of our own hearing and that of others is one of the most important areas in which musicians can serve. All too often, this task is left to "others" or to specialists in the remediation of hearing problems. Even the deaf (total hearing loss) can be taught to appreciate and attend to some of the physical vibrations created by music. A number of organizations have played a vital role in educating the public, diagnosing hearing loss and treating those with hearing losses.[8]

> **EVOKED POTENTIAL: Also known as "evoked response" is an electrical potential recorded from the nervous system of a human or other animal following presentation of a stimulus. In this chapter the stimulus is auditory.**

---

[8] *Department of Veterans Affairs staff at Mountain Home, TN, Long Beach, CA, Nashville, TN. The Audiology Primer for Students and Health Care Professionals, 3rd edition. Pg 39-40 Retrieved May 14, 2009, from East Tennessee State University Web site:* http://etsu.edu/crhs/commdis/audiology/audiologyebook.aspx

Musicians earplugs™ are custom fit hearing protection that are designed to replicate the natural response of the open ear. Sound heard with these filtered earplugs has the same quality as the original, only at a reduced sound pressure level. There are also some filtered "one-size-fits-most" earplugs. The over-the-counter and general use ear protectors are effective but muffle all sounds, including speech.[9]

Early Intervention

Early identification and intervention of hearing loss during the critical language learning age has many positive outcomes. Universal newborn hearing screening is now possible with advances in equipment, research, and experience. Otoacoustic Emissions (OAEs) and Auditory Brainstem Response (ABR) are recommended by the National Joint Committee on Infant Hearing Screening.[10] The internet may be consulted for further information on these organizations. The goal of this program is implementation before 6 months of age. It is no longer unusual for these early identified children with hearing loss to be fit with hearing aids by age 3 *months* instead of 3 *years*.

Although early identification of hearing loss is ideal, some hearing losses develop at a later age or are progressive at the onset. A variety of recommended hearing screening methods are used, appropriate for the age group being screened. These are available in several venues from schools, senior citizens centers, medical doctor's offices, and health fairs.

The Veterans Administration audiology program was established to furnish audiometric examinations, treatment and guidance to veterans of World War II. The scope of its treatment was subsequently widened to include all military service related hearing disabilities. Its activities have provided excellent research and information on hearing loss and the development of programs to aid persons who are hearing impaired.

Hearing Aids

When one thinks of hearing loss, it is common to also think of hearing aids as a sort of universal cure. This is not always the case. Hearing aids have made tremendous advances from the days of the now old fashioned "ear trumpets!" While they seemed to help the hard of hearing in some cases, they were bulky and cosmetically quite unattractive; especially to younger people. The modern hearing aid is a miniature electronic sound system. However, instead of amplifying the full frequency spectrum, audiologists and hearing appliance man-

---

[9] *Etymotic Research, Killion, M. Retrieved April 27, 2009 Web site:*
http://www.etymotic.com/ephp/erme-ihp.aspx

[10] *Joint Committee on Infant Hearing (JCIH) members (2007): American Academy of Audiology, the American Speech-Language-Hearing Association, the American Academy of Otolaryngology-Head and Neck Surgery, the American Academy of Pediatrics, the Alexander Graham Bell Association for the Deaf and Hard of Hearing, the Council on Education of the Deaf, and the Directors of Speech and Hearing Programs in State Health and Welfare Agencies.*

ufacturers are chiefly concerned with amplifying those frequencies associated with speech. Although sensorineural hearing loss implies that some neural pathways are no longer functional, those paths that continue to function may still be stimulated by amplification of those frequencies. Even though hearing losses are often progressive and may continue to affect more and more frequencies over time, today's technology allows for some **equalization** of the audible spectrum for those with hearing loss.

Hearing aid computer chips have an available frequency response range from 100–7000 Hz. Adjustments to shape the gain at each frequency band allow for a more exact fitting of the configuration of the individual's hearing loss. This is no small accomplishment. Those who have not heard these frequencies at normal amplitudes for some time are very happy with the results. Consonants become crisp and clear again, and it becomes easier to understand what people are saying. Music listening is yet another bonus. It stands to reason that if frequencies that have formerly been damped are regained for speech, they are concomitantly regained for listening to music as well.

Some higher end hearing aids, with multiple memories, allow the addition of a music program. There are several changes in the algorithms for this program including increasing amplification in the low frequencies to provide the richness and fullness of music and refraining from overly compressing the audible spectrum. It is not unusual for audiologists fitting hearing aids on musicians to have patients bring a favorite CD to use in the adjustment the hearing aid's program.

With a hearing aid, there is an adjustment period of "getting used to" a rather new kind of hearing. Soft sounds that were once inaudible become audible. Certain of the newer styles of hearing aids are "open fit," and they are appropriate for some configuration of hearing loss. Singers prefer this style, as their own voice doesn't sound as if they are "in a barrel."

Implantable Hearing Devices

Some people with hearing loss in the middle ear have found great benefit from a Bone Anchored Implant (BAHA). Persons with chronic draining ears that cannot wear traditional hearing aids or those with craniofacial abnormalities especially benefit from these devices.

Cochlear Implants (CI) place electrodes in the cochlea. Research has indicated this is an option to hear when traditional hearing aids do not benefit for those with profound losses. They have been so effective, the criteria for implantation has been expanded to those with a severe hearing loss. It is now common to see bilateral cochlear implants. This is also a recommended treatment for those with Auditory Neuropathy/Auditory Dys-synchrony. Specific suggestions for music for people with CI are readily available.[11]

> EQUALIZATION: Tailoring the audible frequency spectrum to particular intensity levels. In this case, amplifying differentially those frequencies that audiological testing shows need boosting.

---

[11] Chasin, M. (2009) Hearing Loss and Musicians, San Diego: Plural Publishing.

With gradual or progressive hearing loss, people simply cannot remember hearing any other way, and therefore often do not consider themselves as having a hearing problem. Their family and friends have gradually gotten used to making accommodations for the person with a hearing loss. The overriding reason cited for the delay in purchasing hearing aids is cost. The vast majority of Americans with hearing loss (95%) have their hearing loss treated with hearing aids. Only about 5% of hearing loss in adults can be improved through medical or surgical treatment, although this number is rising with the advent of more implantable devices. Federal guidelines and state laws provide protection to insure that people with hearing losses amenable to medical treatment are provided that opportunity.[12]

Coping Strategies and Summary

It must be reiterated that a hearing aid will not restore "normal hearing." We hear with our brains, not our ears. The entire periphery and auditory processing system must be intact or amenable to amplification, to cognitively interpret speech sounds.

Coping strategies appropriate to helping a person with auditory problems would include: 1) getting their attention, 2) getting closer (approximately, a three foot distance) before speaking, 3) facing the person to allow for better sound and speechreading and, 4) turning off background noises. Raising the amplitude of the voice to compensate for further distance only serves to distort the sound. Actually, speaking *slightly* slower also helps.

Our hearing is a precious gift. It's easy to forget just how precious. As musicians and teachers of music, we must make it one of our causes to impress upon our students to appreciate their sense of audition in this age of over amplified music and increased use of personal listening devices via ear buds. The fashion of using one's skin as a sound sensor, while "fun" in the short term will, in most situations, fatigue the hearing apparatus to the point of eventual hearing loss. The losses one can incur far outweigh any short-term pleasure that is gained by such listening habits.

---

[12] *Better Hearing Institute. Kochkin, S. Retrieved April 27, 2009 Web Site:* http://www.betterhearing.org/hearing_solutions

DISCUSSION QUESTIONS FOR CHAPTER SIX

1. Describe the range of hearing loss.

2. If a wind player complains of earache each time the instrument is played, what might you suspect?

3. Explain why progressive hearing loss is quite difficult to diagnose.

4. Discuss the differences between sensorineural and conductive deafness.

5. Discuss the loud music, musicians and audiences at rock concerts. What can you tell these people about hearing loss? Are there strategies that will help make them believe you?

6. What is meant by "conservation of hearing?"

7. How will you know if you are the victim of hearing loss?

The Perception of Music
CHAPTER 7

AURAL PERCEPTION

Aural perception is the sensory translation of physical vibrations that occur in nature. Because each person has experienced different things and learned differently, perception is a complex subject. As has been previously stated, "We 'hear' with our brain, not our ears." The auditory cortex processes sound at different levels.

Throughout history, people have agreed upon certain labels for various aural sensations. Terms like "timbre," that describe envelope and harmonic complexity, are used to portray musical perceptions. Furthermore, sounds are often defined as high or low, loud or soft, fast or slow, long or short. There are whole dictionaries devoted to specialized music terms, in many languages, that are labels for extremely involved and sophisticated aural perceptions.

Aural perception has been the subject of study in many diverse disciplines. Historians have looked carefully at the discovery and usage of intervals and scales, some of which led to the development of our modern twelve-semi-tones-per-octave musical system.[1] Reasons for the development and uses of various musical systems have been scrutinized by musicologists and Ethnomusicologists.[2] Physicians and anatomists have studied the mechanics of the ear, nervous system and brain in order to describe the physical aspects of the perception process.[3] Psychologists and musicians have studied the reactions of organisms to physical stimuli.[4] Sociologists have studied cultures and groups of people to collect data about

---

[1] *Many such works were published in the nineteenth century, including the treatise by Helmholtz (noted in many other places in this book), "On the Sensation of Tone." One of the clearest rationalizations for the use of various intervals and scale systems was the work of the nineteenth-century German sociologist and amateur violinist, Max Weber:*
Weber, Max, The Rational & Social Foundations of Music, translated and edited by D. Martindale, et al., (Southern Illinois University Press, 1954).

[2] *Sachs, Curt, Real-Lexicon der Musikinstrumente, Zugleich ein Polyglossar fur des gesamte Instrumentengebiet, Reg. and enlarged ed., (New York: Dover Publications, 1961).*
Nettle, Bruno, Theory & Method in Ethnomusicology, (New York: The Free Press, 1964).

[3] *Bekesy, G., Experiments in Hearing, (New York: McGraw Hill Book Company, 1960). Ruch, Theodore, et. al., Neurophysiology, second ed., (Philadelphia: W. B. Saunders Company, 1965). Stevens, Charles F., Neurophysiology: A Primer, (New York: John Wiley and Sons, Inc., 1966).*

[4] *Farnsworth, Paul R., The Social Psychology of Music, (Iowa State University Press, 1969). Madsen, C.K., Greer, R.D. & Madsen, C. H., Research in Music Behavior, (New York: Teachers College Press, 1975).*

> **AURAL PERCEPTION: The sensory translation of physical vibrations which occur in nature.**

85

certain preferences for various aural stimuli (scales, intervals, melodies, forms, etc.) with which to make observations about the cultural uses of music.[5]

Researchers in the fields of Perception, Psychoacoustics and Psychophysics have attempted to link findings from more than one discipline, in order to more completely describe our aural sense.[6] The observations of all these professional researchers are attempts to describe the perceptual process. The search for how synaptic electrochemical energy is converted into thoughts, feelings, emotions and impressions goes on. Since our study of these processes must be limited, this chapter will trace a broad path across many of these disciplines. Let's look first at where the auditory impulses travel once they leave the cochlea of the inner ear.

THE PHYSICAL PROCESS

The **auditory nerve** is a bundle of approximately 30,000 nerve fibers (called neurons). This tiny "cable" of neurons (about one millimeter in diameter), runs through the center of the cochlea. There, individual neurons break away from the main bundle and form **synapses** (junctions) with the hair cells in the organ of Corti. Following the auditory nerve from the cochlea in the opposite direction, auditory signals are carried by neurons into the central nervous system through various "stages" before terminating in an orderly fashion in the temporal lobes of the brain.[7] Here is a short explanation of how these neurological signals are transmitted.

Nerve Cells

Neurons are single nerve cells consisting of a **cell body** with a number of tiny fibers extending from it, called **dendrites**. A long fiber called the **axon**, measuring from a few millimeters up to about a meter in length (in certain areas of the human body) extends from the cell body, and has on its ends, branches called terminal arbors. Dendrites of one cell body lie in close proximity to (but do not touch) the terminal arbors of another neuron. When a neurological signal is sent from a cell body through the axon to its terminal arbors, the signal, in the form of electrochemical energy, "jumps" to the dendrite of another cell body. Thus the chain is continued. This tiny space between dendrites and terminal arbors is called a synapse. The electro-chemical interaction between the two is synaptic activity.

AUDITORY NERVE: The major portion of the eighth cranial nerve. It transmits encoded auditory signals to the central nervous system and eventually to both the right and left temporal lobes of the brain.

SYNAPSE: The space between dendrites of one neuron and the terminal arbors of the axon of another neuron. While these neural "branches" do not touch, electrical signals pass across these gaps.

NEURON: A complete nerve cell consisting of a nerve body, dendrites, an axon and terminal arbors.

CELL BODY: The portion of the neuron which contains the cell nucleus and cytoplasm and from which protrude the dendrites.

DENDRITE: The branches of the neuron body which receive electrical signals from the terminal arbors of other neurons.

AXON: The long part of the neuron (nerve cell) which transfers impulses from the nerve body to the tips of its arbors.

---

[5] Laws, George M., Native American Balladry, (Philadelphia: American Folklore Society, 1950). Thieme, Darius L., African Music, A Briefly Annotated Bibliography, (Washington, D.C.: Library of Congress, Reference Department, Music Division, 1964).

[6] Sternbach, Richard A., Principles of Psychophysiology, (New York: Academic Press, 1966). Roederer, J.G., The Physics & Psychophysics of Music, (London: English Universities Press, 1974).

[7] Ruch, et al., op. cit., Chapter 18.

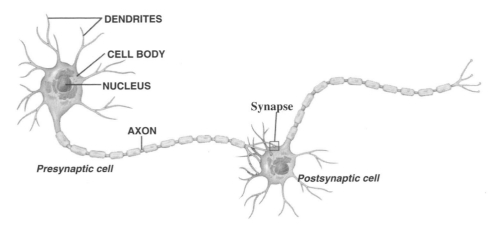

Figure 7-1. The anatomy of a neuron. The cells that compose the nervous system are called "neurons." A neuron in the brain may be a few thousandths of an inch in length, while a neuron extending to the extremities of the body from the brain can be up to three or four feet in length (though the cell body of the neuron would be less than one hundredth of an inch in diameter).

The neurological signal is electrical and is caused by chemical configurations that create a very small voltage (potential) and thus cause current to flow through the neurons. Electricity travels at nearly the speed of light. Therefore, the energy flow through neurons is extremely rapid. There is a mechanism in neurons that, in certain instances, accelerates the nerve impulses to even greater speeds (in higher animals and man) for quick decision making and, thus, survival. However, once a nerve has "fired," it must go through a period of rest so that the chemicals involved can return to their steady state potential (inactive state). This rest or refractory period takes between one and three thousandths of a second.

Nerve cells have only two states—active and inactive. Because of this, an individual neuron pulse cannot carry information concerning the intensity of a stimulus. The neuron pulse can only carry information about whether a stimulus of sufficient energy is present or not. Neurons respond to the intensity of a stimulus by the rate at which they fire. As a stimulus increases, the rate of firing increases. The nervous system codes sound's amplitude into the frequency of neural discharge.

In animal organisms, the nervous system is the message network that controls behavior. Even simple animals such as the freshwater hydra and the jellyfish have nervous systems of sorts. In higher order animals and especially in humans, a much more complex nervous network exists. Thought processes, sensory input, motor activity and all those body functions termed involuntary are monitored and controlled by the nervous system. The brain, spinal cord, and the thousands of neurons that extend out from the spinal cord to every part of the body, are part of a complex electrochemical network that receives, stores and sends messages to and from all organs in the body.

The Central Nervous System

Man's brain is a actually a complex of organs and is subdivided first into three components, each with its own areas of control within the body. They are the **cerebrum**, the **cerebellum** and the **brain stem** or reticular formation. The human brain contains many billions of nerve cells (neurons) that audit and control most body functions. Reflexive action, processed at the spinal cord, is the most notable exception.

Signals from the cochlea enter the central nervous system, pass first through the brain stem, then through the midbrain and ascend into the temporal lobes of both hemispheres of the brain. Neurons from both ears are interconnected through synapses at an early point in their path (the brain stem), thus allowing stereo aural sensory perception.[8]

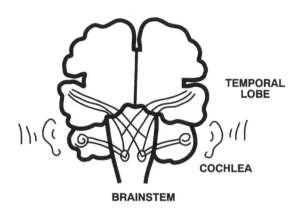

Figure 7-2. Nerve impulses travel to the temporal lobes along routes determined by their frequencies. More impulses cross to the opposite hemisphere than are processed on the side on which the sounds are heard.

The neurons of the central auditory nervous system process the signals sent from the cochlea by sending portions of the signal via different routes to the temporal lobes. Neurons in one path respond to high tones, while those along a different path respond to low tones. In other words, structures within the brain along the auditory pathway follow the same frequency coding by spatial relationships (Place Theory) that frequency coding follows along the basilar membrane in the cochlea.

The cerebral cortex (covering of the cerebrum) or "grey matter" is possibly the most interesting of the brain's components because it contains distinctive electrical properties that can be monitored to give clues about sensory input and thought processes.[9] The cortex contains over ten billion nerve cells and, through

CEREBRUM: The largest part of the brain. It is largely composed of "grey matter" which is due to the grey color of the neuron bodies. The cerebrum functions as a sensory interpreter, controls all voluntary muscles and is the center of all mental functions associated with reasoning, intelligence, judgments and emotions. Four areas of the cerebral cortex have been identified with various functions. These areas, called lobes, are named frontal lobe, parietal lobe, temporal lobe and occipital lobe.

CEREBELLUM: Controls skeletal muscles and plays an important part in the coordination of voluntary muscles. The cerebellum receives and sends impulses but is not a reflex center, although it may serve to intensify some reflexes and depress others. It is composed of neurons with large and long axons.

BRAIN STEM: A collective term for all the brain parts except the cerebellum and cerebrum. The brain stem includes the medulla, midbrain, thalamus, hypothalamus and pituitary glands. Interconnections between these areas form the reticular formation.

---

[8] *For an excellent nontechnical treatment of auditory neurology and aural perception, see:* The Mind, Life Science Library, *(New York: Time, Inc., 1964).*

[9] *This section and* Brain Waves and Music *are based upon an article by the author titled "Brain-waves & Biofeedback,"* Journal of Music Therapy, XII, No. 2, Summer, 1975.

synaptic routing, there are more possible combinations of neural pathways than there are atoms in the entire universe! This intricate organ shows both a continuous and rhythmic alteration of electrical potential, and a variety of more localized, larger microvoltage responses. The continuous flow of electrical output is called "spontaneous" activity because it is always present in living organisms. The localized responses are called "evoked" because their presence seems closely associated with the input of our senses.[10]

A closer examination of the physical makeup of the cerebral cortex will reveal the nature of these brainwaves. The cortex of the cerebrum is divided into two hemispheres (halves)—a right hemisphere and a left hemisphere. Each hemisphere has been divided into four lobes; frontal, parietal, temporal and occipital. Together, these four lobes make up one hemisphere of the cerebral cortex. Each of the brain's hemispheres is nearly a mirror of the other, yet each hemisphere seems to specialize in controlling certain kinds of thoughts and actions.

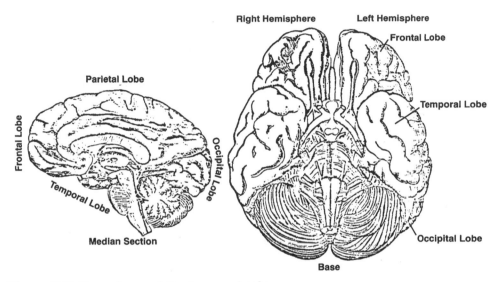

Figure 7-3. Two views of the human brain.

To state accurately all the functions of each of the four lobes would be impossible, since the human brain is still in the early stages of being mapped. It may generally be said that areas of the occipital lobes are associated with the input of visual stimuli, parts of the parietal lobes with speech and motor activities, portions of the frontal lobes with complex thought processes, and temporal lobes for auditory processing. These descriptions, however, are somewhat incorrect or at least misleading, because complex interactions between lobes and hemispheres are highly probable before, during and after each portion of a human behavior or thought. Each lobe in both hemispheres of the cerebral cortex generates both "spontaneous" and "evoked" brainwaves throughout the life span of the organism.

---

[10] *In recent times, the actions of the cortex have been studied by observing blood gas levels and even more recently, by observing cortical activity in real time, using an MRI (Magnetic Resonance Imaging). Check on the internet: "Brain's Responses to Music"*

Binaural Hearing

There are several benefits of symmetrical hearing either naturally, or in the case of hearing loss, for binaural amplification. Improved ability to understand speech in noise is also referred to as "binaural squelch." The central auditory system can "squelch" the noise to some extent when hearing from both ears.[11] Binaural loudness summation is the intensity advantage in loudness perceived by two ears over the one ear. Neither ear has to be as loud to obtain the same loudness perception with both.[12] **Sound localization** in the horizontal plane is improved. The head-shadow effect, caused by the head's ability to attenuate high frequency sounds, is reduced. Spatial balance for complex acoustic environments results in increased precision. An ear that receives little auditory stimulation can show reduced speech intelligibility over time. This deprivation effect can be minimized with binaural stimulation. Sound quality is improved with perception of greater "fullness," and with less distortion. Binaural hearing allows for perception of sound across the head rather than "at the ear." This advantage is very important in the enjoyment and perception of music.

Brain Waves and Music

In the recent past, there has been increased interest among educators, therapists, the medical community, and even other professionals in the monitoring of brain waves. Popular national magazines advertise **biofeedback** equipment that allows the monitoring of one's own **electroencephalogram** (EEG) or brain wave patterns, and on the basis of that information, to find a way to change those brain wave patterns. The reasons for doing so run the gamut from the scientific to the seemingly bizarre. Biofeedback has been successfully used to reduce anxiety levels. The incidence and severity of migraine headaches and stress have been diminished in some patients by psychologists and physicians using biofeedback methodology and similar techniques. Biofeedback has been used to reduce stress associated with tinnitus or head noises. Astronauts' attentiveness levels have been monitored from space using telemetric transmission of brain wave signals to mission control. Advertising researchers have monitored the brain waves of television viewers to determine the effects that advertisements have had on the public. There may be a way to actually modify one's own musical behavior using these techniques.

There is a connection between a person's musical behavior and audio signals transmitted from the cochlea of the inner ear through the auditory nerve to the temporal lobes of the brain. Exactly how "perception" and the processing of these musical signals takes place is still a mystery. Findings in recent research have raised the possibility that a person's cortical activity may contain clues to these cognitive aural processes. The area of "attention to music" has been studied.[13]

SOUND LOCALIZATION: Identification of the origin of a sound in space (horzontal or vertical plane).

BIOFEEDBACK: Techniques predicated upon information received from some internal body function (i.e., temperature, heart rate, brain wave rhythm) upon which conscious will is exerted in order to make modifications on the internal process.

ELECTROENCEPHALOGRAM (EEG): The printout or graph of brain wave patterns from an instrument which amplifies electrical fluctuations of the brain more than a billion times. The frequency and amplitude per second of electrical fluctuations are the parameters measured.

---

[11] Mueller, H.G. & Hall, J.W. & (1998) *Audiologists' Desk Reference Volume II Audiologic Management, Rehabilitation, and Terminology.* San Diego: Singular Publishing Group, Inc.

[12] Villchur, E. (2000) *Acoustics for Audiologists.* San Diego: Singular Publishing Group. Inc.

[13] Menen, V. and Sridharan, D., "Neural Dynamics of Event Separation in Music," *Neuron*, Vol. 55, No. 3, August 2, 2007.

It has been found that musicians' brains process music differently than do those who have not studied music.[14] The evoked alpha brain waves of musicians are slower, generally, than those of nonmusicians. After listening to new music, those with musical training are apt to remember it longer and describe it in more detail than those with less musical training. Even though both a musician and a nonmusician may hear the same music, the musician's auditory and neurological complex seems able to process more completely the aural/temporal information it receives.

THE MENTAL PROCESS

Learning plays a large part in determining what is emotionally satisfying or aesthetically pleasing. Because we learn all our lives, each new aural experience is processed on the basis of previous knowledge. We reorganize and restructure our learning to accommodate new information. It would seem that those with more musical experiences would process new music with greater and more complex information sorting processes than those with limited experiences and learning.

It may be said that cognitive elements of music include melody, rhythm, harmony, timbre, form, style and expressive characteristics.[15] All of these elements seem to be processed either simultaneously or alternately while listening to music. Not only are these elements processed passively, but people also have developed likes and dislikes or preferences for certain portions of each musical element, and have done so both personally and culturally.[16]

Consonance and Dissonance

Throughout history, scientists and scholars have tried to determine exactly what constitutes the difference between an aural **consonance** and a **dissonance**. It seems that generally, these labels are learned by what we hear in relation to the labels that have been ascribed to what we hear. Reasons for choices are vague and hard to explain. In antiquity, people probably played their melodies based upon their own perception of harmonic consonance and dissonance. Octaves could have come into usage when men attempted to sing in unison with boys or women and found themselves an octave apart when singing with men.

The determining factor in the degree of consonance and degree of dissonance, reported Helmholtz, had to do with how closely the harmonic series of two fundamental frequencies compared.[17] Of course, the harmonic series of two

---

CONSONANCE: A combination of sounds which seem at repose with each other (without conflict). The absence of "roughness," perceived as "smooth." A subjective term.

DISSONANCE: A combination of sounds which are perceived to be at conflict with each other. Rough or harsh intervals. A subjective term.

---

[14] Wagner, M., "Effect of Music and Biofeedback on the Alpha Brainwave Rhythms and Attentiveness of Musicians and Non-Musicians," Journal of Research in Music Education, Spring, 1975.

[15] Florida Catalog of Music Objectives, Department of Education, Tallahassee, Florida, 1974.

[16] Madsen, C.K., Brittin, R.V., & Capperella-Sheldon, D. A. "An Empirical Method for Measuring the Aesthetic Experience in Music." Journal of Research in Music Education, Spring, 1993, pp. 57-69.

[17] Helmholtz, Herman L.F., On the Sensations of Tone, translation by Alexander J. Ellis, (New York: Dover Publications, 1954), pp. 290-309.

unison pitches are in perfect alignment. There are no conflicts with pairs of tones at the octave. It may be seen in Figure 7-4 that any interval smaller than an octave has partials that cause varying degrees of conflict.

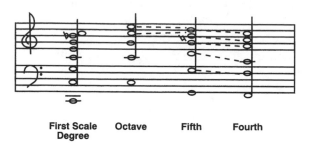

First Scale   **Octave**   **Fifth**   **Fourth**
Degree

Figure 7-4. Conflict between overtones of the harmonic series when each is sounded separately.

While a strong case can be made for a rank ordering of dissonant intervals on the basis of conflict among partials of the harmonic series, it is easy to lose perspective with this information and agree too readily with the above logic. It should be quite obvious that, in fact, preference had been determined well over a thousand years before this theory of consonance and dissonance was explained. It is indeed possible that preference for a particular interval's "purity" might have to do with dissonance within the harmonic series, but certainly not because of this information. Preferences for particular intervals were determined long before the harmonic series was understood.

More recently, research in the area of the psychology of music has lent support to another explanation of what might determine the degrees of consonance and dissonance. If a fixed interval is moved from a high range into a lower range, people tend to rate the interval as being more and more dissonant the lower it gets. This may be one explanation of why the lowest voice in early polyphonic music was sung or played mainly at the intervals of the octave, fifth and fourth (because these intervals have the least harmonic conflict).

Because of historical preferences for certain intervals, tradition must have played an important part in the choice of those intervals that were most often used in music. Harmonic practices were broken by only the most irreverent of our musically "great" composers. Since, historically, it is the practice to maintain a musical system, those who were listeners must have "learned" what to expect. Consequently, the music that was preferred was "correct," and that which was correct was "preferred."

The physicist has shown that the relative intensity of particular harmonics (timbre) within a series must also play a part in determining the degree of consonance between two musical tones.[18] Some of the dissonant harmonic "clashes" may not exist if a particular harmonic has a low intensity or amplitude

---

[18] Culver, Charles A., Musical Acoustics, (New York: McGraw-Hill Book Company, 1965), p. 105.

(remember, the clarinet produces mainly odd numbered partials; Chapter 3). Different voicings and orchestrations produce different degrees of consonance using identical intervals.

Earlier in this chapter, the coding of auditory signals was discussed. The neurological response to tonal stimuli is to try to determine vibration ratios, and to make "sense" or "order" of them. This appears to be a tiring process in which dissonances will probably fatigue a listener sooner than consonances. If so, preferences for consonance may be due in part to this "fatigue effect."[19] It is theorized by some researchers that the brain seems to enjoy the complex process of trying to make order of sensory input. If this theory is plausible, then works of art may be judged positively because the processing and reprocessing of these neurological signals is enjoyable until fatigue sets in. This pleasure may partially explain the aesthetic quality that sets "The Arts" apart from other disciplines.[20] A closer look at the relationships between a **musical interval** and a **musical scale** may help explain the perceptual process in music.

Intervals and Scales

The scientist describes musical intervals mathematically; musicians describe them qualitatively. For the moment, let us pursue the scientific description of intervals.

The scientist explains the octave as two frequencies having relationship to each other in the ratio of 2:1. This simply means that A220 and A440 are octaves, because when the lower figure is multiplied by 2 the vibration rate of the octave above may be determined. Conversely, by dividing the upper figure by 2, the frequency of the lower octave is obtained.

The musical interval of the fifth has a ratio of frequencies that is 3:2. To determine the interval of a perfect fifth, a frequency may be chosen (400 Hz, arbitrarily), multiplied by 3 (400 x 3 = 1200) and the result divided by 2 (1200/2 = 600). By so doing, it may be determined that the frequencies of 400 Hz and 600 Hz are a perfect fifth apart. If one wishes to find a perfect fifth below 400 Hz, divide by 3 (400/3 = 133.3) and multiply the result by 2 (133.3 x 2 = 266.6). Using this method it may easily be determined that 266.6 Hz is a perfect fifth below 400 Hz.

The Greek mathematician, Pythagoras, devised a scale system using the perfect fifth and the octave as its basis.[21] The scale used an ascending projection of perfect fifths (with the necessary dropping of octaves to construct a stepwise scale) until a chromatic scale was completed. Interestingly, scales constructed using this system overshoot the octave by a small amount. Because these scales do not produce a perfect octave, they create sharps equaling one frequency and what

---

[19] Roederer, op. cit., p. 144.

[20] Ibid., p. 23.

[21] Weber, op. cit.

MUSICAL INTERVAL: Any two frequencies with any timbre. Their relationship to each other may be described mathematically as a ratio or described subjectively, i.e., consonant or dissonant.

MUSICAL SCALE: Any group of tones which divide the audible frequency spectrum. Octaves are not essential, though they have been an important interval in most cultures' scales. (A musical scale might be constructed by the equal division of two octaves into seven parts.)

we think of as their enharmonic flat equivalents at a different frequency. Pythagoras was particularly influenced by the ratio of 3:2 because these were numbers of significance in the religion and philosophy of the Greek civilization of his time. As a mathematician, he knew of frequencies but had no sophisticated scientific equipment. Instead, he constructed a chromatic scale using the mathematical relationships of simple ratios.

Even though it is possible to express any interval in terms of a mathematical ratio of frequencies, it would be difficult to conceive of primitive man doing so to build a scale. Musical intervals were in use long before the time of Pythagoras. Possibly the first intervals were determined by the placement of holes on a wooden flute. The intervals of the perfect fifth and its inversion, the perfect fourth, appeared sometime later in history, possibly because they were overblown harmonics on an instrument or because of their particularly consonant sound. From these primitive beginnings, various cultures went on to develop other intervallic relationships by dividing the octave in many different ways. The Chinese created a scale system quite different from that of the Egyptians, and the Hindus conceived yet another kind of scale configuration. There must have been hundreds of scale systems used at various periods throughout history, many of them are still in use. Our occidental, or western scale system, however, probably developed through a series of modifications of the Pythagorean system.

Within the audible frequency spectrum, the construction of any scale system singles out certain frequencies as more important than all other frequencies. A scale may be thought of as any pattern of audible frequencies arranged in an ascending and/or descending order. Possibly the first scales were determined by placing holes on primitive wooden flutes, thereby fixing certain pitches for the player and his or her listeners. One early Greek scale consisted of only three notes. Historians and music scholars hypothesize that the development pattern of the western scale system probably went from the use of the unison to the octave, to the fifth and to the fourth. With the addition of two more tones, the pentatonic scale evolved. Over many hundreds of years and through a combination of social and religious practices and taboos, the Greek modes were developed.

As was previously noted, not all civilizations arrived at a twelve tone division of the octave. Pentatonicism is still practiced in many cultures, while the Arabian peoples have divided the octave into sixteen unequal intervals. In some areas, the quarter tone has become the basis of scale systems, and even within our own culture various other **temperaments** have been tried.

The reasons and methods for arriving at each of these systems is not the concern of this chapter. Many scholars have speculated upon their development.[22]

TEMPERAMENT: Configuration of tones based upon the natural harmonic series that have been adjusted upward or downward to form a particular musical system.

[22] *For example: Moran, H. and Pratt, C.C., "Variability of Judgements on Musical Intervals,"* Journal of Experimental Psychology, IX, 1926, pp. 492-500.
Weber, op. cit.
Ward, D. and Martin, D.W., "Psychophysical Comparison of Just Tuning and Equal Temperament in Sequences of Individual Tones," Journal of the Acoustical Society of America, XXXIII, 1961, pp. 568-588.

What seems important is that we have arrived in the twenty-first century with a scale configuration or system that has evolved through approximately four thousand years of trial and error. The fact that we recognize our scales as "correct" is most certainly a learned phenomenon. Peoples of many other cultures would not agree that our scale system sounds "proper." Since nearly all of our music learning has taken place within the confines of our own scale configuration, we perceive these tones to be "proper, right and correct."

Temperament Systems

To musicians, the term temperament means the deciding upon and adjusting up or down of certain frequencies or intervals from the "pure" or "natural" harmonic series to form a functional scale system. As was stated earlier, primitive temperaments were probably based upon tones that could be produced on the instruments with which they were created. With the development of brass instruments, the harmonic series (obtained on an open horn) played an important role and formed the basis for choosing tones in our musical system. How we arrived at equal temperament in our scale system is quite interesting.

Four temperament systems form an outline that reveals the gradual development of our occidental scale system and tuning.[23] A comparison of the tones in each of these systems will be found at the conclusion of this section in Figure 7-5.

By projecting a series of musical fifths upward, and by dropping octaves when necessary, the Greek mathematician Pythagoras devised a temperament system based entirely upon the ratios of 2:1 for the octave and 3:2 for the perfect (natural) fifth. Because the system overshoots the octaves by an interval labeled "the Pythagorean Comma" (23.5 cents or very nearly a quarter tone), and because the sharp semitones are not enharmonic equivalents of their flat semitone counterparts, practical application of this temperament system presented certain difficulties. The lack of enharmonic equivalency meant that changing keys was impossible without distortion of intervals in the new key. The system has no "mathematically pure" major thirds (those with small whole number ratios). The Pythagorean major third is constructed using a ratio of 81:64. Because of a lack of enharmonicism, only six normal major scales were possible. The others were distorted by enharmonic substitutions. Pythagorean tuning did have, as a theoretical advantage, the pure or "perfect" fifth.

In an attempt to keep the pure perfect fifth and adjust Pythagorean tuning so that a mathematically simpler major third was possible, the "just temperament system" developed. Although this scale system is "pure" within a limited range, its problems are even more abundant than those of the Pythagorean system. Enharmonic equivalence is still not achieved, limiting music to one key.

---

[23] *It is assumed that although scholars speak of Pythagorian, Mean-Tone, Just and Equal tempered scale systems, combinations of these systems and others have in fact been in musical practice from earliest times, due to preference, accident or planning. These four systems are interesting however, from a historical and comparative perspective.*

While modulation is possible, it is not musically "pleasing." Other mathematical complications result, requiring two sizes for intervals using the same letter names, thus hiding frequency differences from musicians trying to read "just" music. While "just" intonation is a theoretically possible system of temperament, it is not practical. Its uses are limited to unaccompanied singing, violin performance and performance using other instruments without fixed pitches.

Historical documents indicate that "mean tone temperament" was in use at the beginning of the sixteenth century. It has been described by some performers as quite satisfying both melodically and harmonically. Recent research indicates, however, that most people cannot hear these minute intervallic changes. This system sacrifices the pure perfect fifth in favor of only one size for each interval. Because the interval of the fifth is slightly smaller than the perfect fifth, major triads sound "flat." However, by projecting a series of these fifths, a smaller (and more pleasing) major third than the Pythagorean major third can be created.

By adjusting or compromising the perfect fifth to achieve a more manageable third, the historical precedent was set for a division of the octave into the now familiar twelve equal semitones. However, mean tone temperament survived well into the nineteenth century in some parts of England as evidenced by the tunings of cathedral organs.[24]

Our present system of temperament had been experimented with since the sixteenth century, but did not find widespread acceptance until the time of Bach, in the seventeenth century. It must be remembered that all church organs in the Western world had been tuned to one of several temperament systems. General acceptance of a new standard meant wholesale revision of fixed pitch instruments and "getting used to" a new sound (temperament). This kind of radical departure from tradition is not easy for any civilization to accept.[25]

The tones of the "equal temperament" scale are obtained by dividing the octave (2:1 ratio) into twelve equal semitones. Computation of these intervals is accomplished by obtaining a ratio for the semitone ($\sqrt[12]{2} = 1.059$). The 12th root of 2 perfectly divides an octave into 12 equal semitones. The mathematics of such a scale division, while interesting, will be left to the physicist and mathematician.[26] Equal tempered semitones have been divided further into "cents," with each chromatic semitone being equal to 100 cents (yielding 1200 cents per octave).

---

[24] *Ely Cathedral, Ely, England, finally tuned its organ to equal temperament in 1923.*

[25] *JS Bach celebrated the equal tempered system by composing "The Well Tempered Clavier," a collection containing a piece for keyboard in every major and minor key; because it was then possible!*

[26] *A concise mathematical explanation of equal temperament and a comparison to other systems may be found in:*
Olsen, Harry F., Musical Engineering, (New York: McGraw-Hill Book Company, 1952), pp. 46-57.
Backus, J., The Acoustical Foundations of Music, (New York: W. W. Norton and Company, Inc., 1969), in: Chapter 8, "Intervals, Scales, Tuning and Temperament," pp. 115-140.

In equal temperament, there are no natural intervals or intervals with small whole number ratios except the unison and the octave. The major advantage of this system is that it allows for modulations between all keys and only one set of interval sizes. Presented in Figure 7-5 is a comparison of the four major temperament systems that have achieved attention and notoriety in historical musical documents of the Western world.

	Pythagorean Temperament	Just Temperament	Mean-Tone Temperament	Equal Temperament
C	0	0	0	0
B#	23.5	0	0	0
D♭	90.2	111.7	117.1	100.0
C#	113.7	70.7	76.1	100.0
D	203.9	203.9	193.2	200.0
E♭	294.1	315.6	310.3	300.0
D#	317.6	274.6	269.2	300.0
F♭	384.4	427.4	427.4	400.0
E	407.8	386.3	386.3	400.0
F	498.0	498.0	503.4	500.0
E#	521.5	457.0	462.4	500.0
G♭	588.3	631.3	620.5	600.0
F#	611.7	590.2	579.5	600.0
G	702.0	702.0	696.6	700.0
A♭	792.2	813.7	813.7	800.0
G#	815.6	772.6	772.6	800.0
A	905.9	884.4	889.7	900.0
B♭	996.1	1017.6	1006.8	1000.0
A#	1019.6	976.5	965.8	1000.0
C♭	1086.3	1129.3	1124.0	1100.0
B	1109.8	1088.3	1082.9	1100.0
C	1200.0	1200.0	1200.0	1200.0

Figure 7-5. Cents difference from C, in a scale projected upward. Data includes all intervals for the four major temperament systems.

Until now, acoustical principles have been described chiefly in the language of physics and mathematics, while musical sensations have been described subjectively. A relatively new field called Psychoacoustics seeks to bring together information from acoustical, neurological and perceptual areas in order to better explain aural sensation, emotions, preferences for certain aspects of music, aural learning, and even aesthetic phenomena. Research that combines related aspects of more than one these disciplines will hopefully result in new theories and explanations of human aural perception.

DISCUSSION QUESTIONS FOR CHAPTER SEVEN

1. What is meant by "perception" of sound?

2. Describe how electrochemical energy is transmitted from the cochlea to the temporal lobe of the brain. How are intensity and frequency encoded?

3. What are brain waves and what clues do they offer in describing the listening process?

4. How does learning affect our preferences?

5. Describe the concept of consonance and dissonance.

6. What is a musical scale?

7. Discuss what areas the relatively new field of Psychoacoustics tries to describe.

Part III

The electronic production and reproduction of sound is unique in an introductory book on acoustics for musicians; yet in this age of digital stereo and surround sound, the reproduction of sound has great bearing on the making of music. The music recording (music technology) industry is now quite a lot larger than the music making industry. Therefore musicians need to have at least basic information in this area. Additionally, some who start as performing musicians, educators or therapists may eventually find more occupational fulfillment in certain areas of the music technology business. Most musicians should simply like to know how their sound system works. Electronic musical instruments and their (MIDI) interfacing devices are not discussed in many acoustical texts, yet, musicians should know about how these instruments work and what possibilities they generate for now, and for the future of music. The marriage of some familiar technological tools is also noted, such as the merging of the PC, television, the MP3 player, the GPS, and the cell phone. Video and audio are combining, and soon we will access our computers through our high definition, 16 x 9 picture ratio, widescreen video monitors. Music listening has changed; and quite drastically. There are many implications here for educators and therapists.

Websites for further information are listed here.

Chapter 8

http://en.wikipedia.org/wiki/Sound_recording_and_reproduction

http://amplioaudio.blogspot.com/2007/05/short-history-of-audiovideo-technology.html

Chapter 9

http://www.tedscott.co.uk/audiowisehome.html

http://en.wikipedia.org/wiki/Analog_sound_vs._digital_sound

Chapter 10

http://en.wikipedia.org/wiki/Digital_recording

http://www.musiq.com/recording/digaudio/index.html

http://audacity.sourceforge.net/manual-1.2/tutorial_basics_1.html

Chapter 11

http://emusictips.com/

http://www.electronicmusicproduction.net/

Chapter 12

http://audio.tutsplus.com/tutorials/production/creating-rich-soundscapes-with-organic-electronic-sounds/

http://www.archive.org/details/Copter_-_Various_Electronic_Sounds

Foundations of Sound Reproduction

CHAPTER 8

BEGINNINGS IN AUDIO TECHNOLOGY

Audio technology has almost certainly been a concern of humankind throughout the pre-history and history of civilization. It is likely that the ancestors of modern man created primitive musical instruments with the intent of imitating sounds heard in nature. Archeological sites often reveal the remnants of flutes made of animal bone, clay objects that may have been used as drums, and images of stringed and other instruments inscribed on shards of pottery. It is not difficult to imagine how the use of a whistle or flute to imitate a birdcall could quickly become a form of entertainment and pleasure for the player of such an instrument. Or, how the playing of a drum prior to a hunt, in an attempt to imitate the sounds of hoof-beats, could eventually be associated with a sense of spirituality and perhaps well being, especially if previous hunts were successful. In order to enhance the efficacy of the ritual or the quality of the performance, more durable and more musical materials were most likely sought and experimented upon. This, in essence, was music technology in action.

A distinction must be drawn here, as the intent of this chapter is to present an overview of mans' attempt to create machines that recreate music. While the history of musical instrument making is a fascinating subject, efforts here concern the desire to "recycle music," making one performance available again and again. Carillons and water wheels were some of the first devices designed to automatically play music. However, these instruments were primarily one-of-a-kind devices and not available for general use.

The goal of creating personal, commercially produced and publicly available music players was realized during the Renaissance (ca. the 14th–17th centuries).

Using clock mechanisms, music boxes were created that allowed disks, with raised nubs or pins, placed in arrays that recreated musical rhythm, to come into contact with specialized bells, metal-toothed combs or tuned strings. Setting the device in motion caused the tone **generators** to vibrate in patterns and play well-known songs.

> **GENERATOR: A device that converts mechanical energy to other forms of energy, usually electrical in nature.**

Historically, these devices were quite popular, and underwent many modifications, including the addition of other sound producers and the use of interchangeable disks. Their development continued well into the 19th century. Yet improvements to these devices in no way lessened the desire to create "talking machines" that captured and played back analog sound.

Since the industrial revolution and especially since the 1850s, a great many social, cultural, economic and technological changes have taken place. At the time of America's Civil War, people walked, rode horses or drove carts pulled by animals if they went anywhere, and consequently, by today's standards, life was centered very close to home. Unless a musician lived nearby, music wasn't heard by many people. It especially didn't get heard by those who labored for a living, on farms or as tradesmen in towns and villages, unless they sang, of course. Those who lived in the vicinity of an instrumental musician were lucky indeed, because into their lives came the precious commodity—music!

Humankind has used sacred songs to enhance worship, and folk songs to accompany manual labor. Sadly, very often, music of the "formal tradition" was reserved for society's elite. Yet, by the end of the American Civil War, now free men and their families, began moving away from the rural south; north to the cities, or west, to find farms of their own, or work on the railroads. There was also a migration south by northerners (called carpetbaggers, because of how they carried their meager belongings). As America's population began to change demographically, its music also began to change. America's working class began to have "leisure time." Music no longer belonged to the rich, elite landowner, but to the working man looking for a way to express himself, his hopes, his fears, his worries, and as a way to amuse himself and his friends after a hard day's work.

Isn't it unfortunate that we don't have recordings of former slaves singing joyously of their freedom, or solemnly about their lives ahead? What would the first blues or the field hollers of share croppers reveal? Early western settlers on the move, singing "My Home's in Montana," "Clementine," "Look Down, Look Down, That Lonesome Road" preserved information related to their daily lives in their songs. The discovery of recordings of railroad work crews singing their work songs in time with the hammer, pounding spikes into ties while laying mile after mile of steel rail in the searing heat of the desert's sun, would truly be an important find. Yet, it can't happen. There were no recordings then. What we have are old men's memories, and they sing their songs for us like they think they used to be sung, or old folks teach younger singers who then try to imitate the old songs; but without the benefit of having really been there.

First Recordings

A fantastic new technological marvel made the recording of pianists possible in the late 1800s. It became known as the "player piano!" Through a system of bellows and vacuum pumps, the levers (keys) of a piano could be made to move, commanded by a series of holes in a long roll of paper. Performers sat at a "master" piano and punched holes in a "master roll" as they played. Then, duplicate rolls were cut, and the world's first audio recording device was born! Performance speed and some dynamic changes were also able to be manipulated. Those who owned one or found themselves in the proximity of a player piano could listen to a reasonable facsimile of a musician's keyboard performances. How lucky we are today to have preserved the playing of Scott Joplin performing his own rags, Serge Rachmaninoff playing his works, both on piano rolls, and of course, the performances of many others during the late nineteenth century and even on into the "roaring twenties."

Interestingly enough, this "player piano technology" didn't end here. The military band of the Civil War period had been transforming itself into one kind of popular music in America's larger cities. City parks, amusement parks and the like, often had band concerts as standard fare. Those who heard these concerts developed an appetite for music. Bands were few and far between, and the player piano and soon the "band organ" began showing up in amusement parks (many were placed in the center of the carousel). Band organs (and their relative, the Calliope) were a unique form of player piano, with roots back to the days of music box technology. This variety of mechanical musical playback instrument was most often a piano or organ that also played real drums, marimbas, violins and other acoustical instruments, using a series of levers—all by automation! Band organs were fitted with player piano-like rolls and could be played by inserting a coin. Thus, the "juke-box" industry was born[1]. Some could even be found in the saloons of the west and southwest.

The purchase of one of these "machines" was less expensive than paying a live musician or musicians over a long period of time. From a saloon owner's point of view, it was nice that these music machines made enjoyable music, but it was nicer that they were "cheaper" in the long run, than hiring musicians. Operating expenses could be reduced. Imagine, over a century ago, musicians were being put out of work by recording technology. This has become a recurring theme for performing musicians in our recent music history.

The Talking Machine

"Speech has become, as it were, immortal," proclaimed the Scientific American magazine, more than one hundred years ago, upon learning of Thomas Alva Edison's invention of the phonograph. "Music," it added, almost as an afterthought, "may be crystallized as well!"[2]

As early as 1857, Leon Scott, a Frenchman, constructed a device that he called "The Phonoautograph," that recorded the movements of a **diaphragm**, as a wavy line on the smoked surface of a rotating glass cylinder. Twenty years

DIAPHRAGM: A thin membrane or disk that receives and transmits transverse acoustic vibrations.

[1] *Today, it is not easy to find a band organ, but the next time there is a fair or amusement park in your proximity, go to the carousel and look in its center. A band organ may very well be making the music.*

[2] Music Educators Journal, *December, 1977, Vol. 64, No. 4, pp. 52-59.*

later, in 1877, Edison discovered that this process could be reversed, and the original sound vibration could be recreated. He attached a stylus to a diaphragm at the small end of a large, cone-shaped horn. The pressure of his voice on the diaphragm forced the stylus to make indentations on a sheet of tinfoil wrapped around a hand-cranked cylinder. By simply attaching a thinner diaphragm to the horn, the stylus was able to reproduce the original sound, with surprising accuracy. Those who first heard Edison's talking machine must have marveled at humankind's ingenuity. Although electricity had been harnessed with the invention of the telegraph in 1836, it had not been put to practical use in the 1870s; yet, it's interesting to note that it did not play a role in the early development of the recording process.

Sound had been frozen in time—and the recording industry was born. In the late 1880s a German immigrant, Emile Berliner, developed the first flat-disk recordings, made of zinc. A coating of fat on the original disk permitted an acid bath to form the sound grooves that had been dug out by a recording stylus. The next two decades saw the formation of the Victor Talking Machine Company, the London Gramophone Company, and the Columbia Phonograph Company; and the developing of a growing consumer market for recordings of famous singers, band ensembles, pianists and other musicians.

At the dawn of the twentieth century, the American consumer was quite a different person. Industrialization of our country was taking place and factories needed workers. The Wright brothers were constructing a flying machine in their bicycle shop in Dayton, Ohio. Alexander Graham Bell was tinkering with the telephone. Henry Ford was designing an assembly line for his automobile factory. It was the flowering of the "machine age." Many people now worked for wages instead of growing what was needed on farms, and factory workers had money to spend on goods that were being manufactured. As the age of industrialization was ushered in at the beginning of the twentieth century by Henry Ford, Andrew Carnegie and other industrial giants, a new "machine society" was developing. The stage was certainly set for mass communication to find the

American consumer, and vice versa. During this time the recording industry grew and grew. The invention of the "horseless carriage" made it possible to bring musicians to the city to record their music. The industrialization of our country continued, with an increase in manufacturing on the horizon, due to the requirements for machinery created by World War I (1914–1918). As our need for machines increased, our labor force increased, workers worked harder and harder, earned more money, and spent it on increasingly more labor saving devices and leisure time activities. The recording industry thrived, and the American consumer learned to like "popular" music, as well as to appreciate music of a more serious nature. An exciting new invention in the 1920s created quite a boon to the recording companies and caused them to expand their markets even further. The invention was an electrical device called the radio!

Radio

Imagine: broadcasting sound for miles, and with no wires. Radio was the listening medium of choice during the 1920s. Families gathered around their radios, nightly, and among other things, listened to broadcasts of live bands. And, although it would be twenty more years until records could be broadcast, what could be more natural than to buy music on records that one had heard "live," on radio broadcasts!

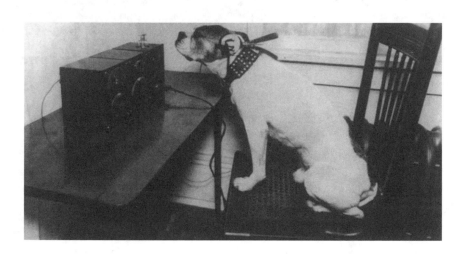

AM: Amplitude modulation. The amplitude or power of a wave of radio energy is electronically encoded with another signal (music, speech), so that broadcast content can be transmitted.

FM: Frequency modulation. The frequency (number of cycles per second) of radio energy is electronically encoded with another signal (music, speech) so that the broadcast content can be transmitted.

ELECTROMAGNETIC ENERGY: Waves of magnetic and electric energy that move together through space.

The first commercial radio broadcasts were "**AM.**" "**FM**" is standard fare now, and satellite radio is now gaining a foothold with the consumer. Regardless of these differentiations, all radio broadcasts rely upon similar systems.

Terrestial radio broadcasts (those emanating from Earth and not from a satellite) require the manipulation of either the amplitude or the frequency of an electromagnetic signal sent from a transmitter (the broadcast tower) and collected by a receiver—your radio!). The transmitter and receptor can be hundreds and even thousands of miles apart because electromagnetic signals travel at the speed of light and can carry energy through the vacuum of space. Sounds such as music and dialog are used to vary **electromagnetic energy** called the

carrier signal so that that those sounds are encoded within the frequency or amplitude of the carrier signal. Your radio receives the encoded electromagnetic energy and then decodes the encoded **signal** from the carrier signal. The signal is then amplified and sent to the speakers of your radio.

Satellite radio works by encoding a carrier signal with a digitized audio signal. That signal is transmitted to a geosynchronous (stationary) satellite high above the Earth. The satellite, due to its height, is able to transmit the signal back to Earth over a very broad area. Because of the digital nature of the encoded signal, information related to specific receivers, such as those in individual automobiles, can be included in the broadcast signal and can be used to lock and unlock the receivers, making paid subscription services possible.

In the 1920s, the music business grew tremendously with the establishment of commercial radio broadcasts. Listeners across entire continents were simultaneously exposed to the music performed by the most popular orchestras and dance bands in the major cities. Conversely, rural musicians, isolated geographically from the large cities, gained ever-increasing audiences via radio broadcasts.

The music business had never been better. In fact, because of the growth in popularity of recorded music, the legacy of that era is a rich recorded chronicle of the best music and musicians of the time. In 1925, the major recording companies converted from mechanically recording music using acoustic recording horns and cutting needles, to the "electrical" process of preserving music, relying on microphones that translated changes in air pressure to analogous variations in electrical signals. This was accomplished by using air pressure to lessen or increase the density of tightly packed carbon granules. As the density of the granules changed, so did the electrical properties of a weak electrical signal passed through the carbon granules. Changes in the electrical signal reflected changes in air pressure created by sounds. Microphones such as these, called "carbon microphones," allowed performers to record with better **fidelity**, and performers no longer had to crowd around a large recording horn. Before the invention of the carbon microphone, musicians had to stand at the large end of a megaphone and sing or play very loudly into it in order to be recorded.[3] To understand what followed technologically, one must know just a little bit about electricity, and how it has helped to improve the process of audio technology since the 1920s.

---

[3] *Acoustic (pre-electrical) records were made in a comparatively small room, with the players grouped in an unconventional fashion according to how they were "picked up" around an enormous recording horn that was attached direct to the disk cutting stylus. The turntable was powered by a weight on a long rope sinking in an open well, and its speed was regulated by a governor, which resembled an anemometer. The recording horn didn't pick up low sounds very well, hence the use of the tuba with a bell front "recording bass" and gimmicks like soloists who would stoop in front of the recording horn, popping up to play their solo, then go back to their former position so as to not interfere with the sounds of other instruments. One "take" lasted 3 minutes 10 seconds, after which a new master (made of wax) was put on the turntable and the power rope was rewound. If there was a mistake, the entire wax had to be discarded and the record had to be cut again. (an anonymous description of how the original "Rhapsody in Blue" by George Gershwin was recorded.)*

CARRIER SIGNAL: Electromagnetic energy at a specific frequency, such as a radio signal, used to carry other frequency related information (such as voice and music), most often over great distances.

SIGNAL: A name given to a pattern of voltage fluctuations passing from one electronic component to another: generally, any disturbance used to convey information.

FIDELITY: Literally, "faithfulness." The degree of accuracy of reproduction of an acoustical phenomenon replicated by an electrical sound system, both in amplitude and in frequency.

THE NATURE OF ELECTRICITY

Electricity is the flow of electrical power or charge. It is a secondary energy source which means that we get it from the conversion of other sources of energy. The electricity we use every day involves the regulated flow of electrons from one atom to another. We control this flow, creating electrical **currents**. The electricity we use travels through **conductors**. Conductors are materials that allow electrons to travel relatively unimpaired. Many materials are conductors, including air and water. Metals are the best conductors. Materials that restrict the flow of electrons are called insulators. Vinyl is an excellent insulator. This is why almost every electrical cable uses both metal and vinyl in its construction. Without the vinyl insulation surrounding strands of metal wire, many of the electrons flowing through the wire in an electrical cable would be drawn to you. Humans are conductors too!

Specialized conductors produce heat. Others produce light. Still others produce motion. In order to accomplish these different kinds of tasks (heat, light and motion), a source of electricity is needed. Batteries are one such source. Batteries most often contain either an acid or alkaline chemical or other oxidizing agent, and two dissimilar metals. The dissimilar metals serve as the + or – poles of the battery. A chemical reaction, resulting from the action of the oxidizing agent in the battery, causes electrons to collect at the negative pole. Connecting a wire between the poles causes those electrons to flow from the negative to the positive pole. Create resistance between the poles, and heat will result. Place a light bulb between the poles and resistance in the filament of the light bulb will generate heat and cause the filament of the light bulb to glow. When the chemical reaction in a battery is complete, the battery is "dead," and all the electrons behave randomly, no longer flowing from the negative to the positive pole of the battery.

Our modern world relies more and more on rechargeable batteries. Rechargeable batteries function similarly to acid or alkaline batteries. However, when the battery is dead, recharging the battery reverses the chemical reaction, forcing electrons back to their original poles. Some energy is lost with each recharge, and ultimately, the chemical in a rechargeable battery is severely weakened and can no longer send electrons back.

For large amounts of steady electrical current, mechanical energy (i.e., falling water, steam or nuclear energy) is converted to electricity by **generators** at local power companies. Generators are giant transducers converting one kind of energy (mechanical) into another (electrical).

Driving mechanical systems by controlling the flow of electrons gave us fixed speed electric motors that were used to accurately turn disks on cutting and playback machines. Not needing to rely on spring driven mechanisms had multiple benefits. Springs quickly lose energy. Electric motors turn as long as power is supplied to them. With electricity, recordings eventually became longer. Fidelity improved and the weight of recording and playback devices decreased.

CURRENT: The measure of the flow of an electric charge through any medium.

CONDUCTOR: Any material that easily allows electric current to pass through it. If little or no current passes through a particular material, it is called an "insulator."

GENERATOR: A transducer of mechanical energy into electrical energy.

Without question, motors were central to important developments in audio recording and reproduction. Equally important to improvements in audio technology were discoveries about the relationship of electricity and magnetism, and experiments involving the storage and flow of electrons within electronic **circuits**. [4]

By understanding that electric currents can exert a force upon one another, even through space, one can begin to conceptualize a **magnetic field**. If a magnet were suspended so it could swing freely, it would line up with the magnetic poles of the earth. The compass is an early use that man made of an electrical field. A bar of iron that has been magnetized has currents (a flow of electrons) that constantly circulate in a particular direction within the bar (Figure 8-1). An iron bar that is not magnetized also has these currents, but they flow in random patterns thus cancelling each other's effect. An electric current or a magnet brought near an iron bar may cause these currents in the bar to line up, or polarize, and the iron will become magnetized.

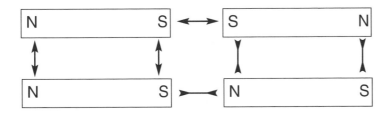

Figure 8-1. Magnetized iron bars. Like poles repel each other; while opposite poles attract.

Magnets, when brought near a wire with current flowing through it, exert a force on the current flow. Also, the current flowing through the wire exerts a force upon the field of the magnet. Thus, two magnetic fields exert forces upon each other and, by using such an arrangement, a metal arm may be caused to turn inside a coil (a winding of wire) through which electricity is flowing.[5] It is upon this principle that electric motors are built. This is an important electrical principle. Before its practical application is discussed however, there is another principle that must be understood. If a coil of wire is moved through a magnetic field, or if a coil is stationary in a magnetic field and the magnitude of the magnetic

---

[4] *Attempts to improve audio fidelity produced some historic oddities. Notable among them are the 1904 "Auxetophone," that used compressed air to increase loudness, and in the early 1920s, the "Flamephone," that used heated air to improve sound reproduction. Others experimented with various materials for gramophone needles, and still others attempted to improve the portability of record players for use in early air ships. In: Pekka, Gronow and Ilpo Saurino. An International History of the Recording Industry. Cassel, 1998, pg. 35.*

[5] *A wire winding, or coil, is an efficient way to bring a great mass of wire into the proximity of a magnet or armature.*

CIRCUIT: The complete path of an electrical current usually including the generator. If the path is broken, the circuit is open; if not, the circuit is closed.

MAGNETIC FIELD: An area under the influence of forces created by the motion of electric charges. This motion may be of electrons in their orbits in particular materials, or electrons passing through conductive materials.

force is changed, an electrical **voltage** is produced in the wire that causes current to flow according to the strength of the magnetic force.[6]

These two important principles form the basis for how audio transducers work. By physically moving a coil in a magnetic field, mechanical motion (motion of the coil) may be converted into electrical potential (voltage). It is this principle upon which some microphones are constructed. By reversing the process; that is, varying the amount of current within the wire coil, a magnet can be physically pushed and pulled through the magnetic field created within a wire coil, thus converting (transducing) electrical potential into mechanical motion. This converse principle forms the basis for the operation of a loudspeaker.

A SIMPLE ELECTRONIC SOUND SYSTEM

Because the voltages that can be created in the coil and magnet of a microphone by variations in sound pressure are so small, a microphone cannot be connected directly to a loud speaker and have the resultant sound made louder. The **signal** or electronic voltage pattern sent from a microphone must first be increased by means of an electronic **amplifier**. Once the signal has been increased, a speaker connected to an amplifier will recreate the sounds, only louder. The system shown in Figure 8-2 is commonly known as a public address system. Using this electronic system, a voice may be amplified so that the sound waves generated are many times louder than the speaker's natural voice. Although in most audio systems the first stage is a "playback" or "music storage" device, these reproducers of stored music will be explained in Chapter 9. A closer look at how each component of this electronic "PA" system functions will help one to understand how an audio system operates.[7]

VOLTAGE: This pertains to the force that electrons experience. It is analogous to the force of water entering a hose, or of the pressure of air from your lungs entering a wind instrument. In the latter case, the current would be the number of air molecules passing a given point inside the horn and the voltage would be a measure of force applied by your lungs.

SIGNAL: A name given to a pattern of voltage fluctuations passing from one electronic component to another: generally, any disturbance used to convey information.

AMPLIFIER: An electronic device that increases the magnitude of voltage fluctuations and current.

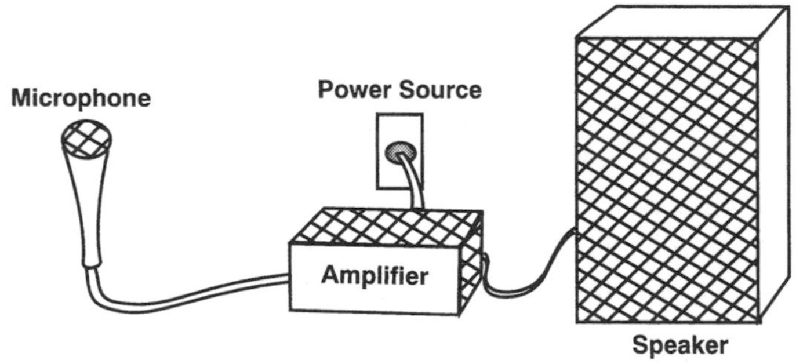

Figure 8-2. A basic electronic sound system. Usually, when these three components are used in combination, they are called a public address system.

---

[6] *For a more thorough treatment of the nature of electricity, the reader is directed to any number of basic physics texts and introductory books about electronics.*

[7] *Current usage is to call the components of an electronic sound system "audio components." In the past they have been called "Hi-Fi" (for high fidelity) components, "stereo" components, and even plain old "sound" components. "Audio" seems the best descriptor for the present time.*

Now that the foundations and physical mechanisms of sound reproduction have been revealed, it's important to carefully examine the more modern elements of audio. This quest begins in the next chapter, with an analysis of the Tools of Analog Sound Reproduction.

DISCUSSION QUESTIONS FOR CHAPTER EIGHT

1. Can you think of any instruments that somehow stored music and played it back before the player piano?

2. Discuss the social ramifications of Edison's "Talking Machine."

3. What were the social ramifications of the introduction of radio.

4. How was the music industry changed by the introduction of batteries, and later, rechargeable batteries?

5. Describe in your own words how an amplifier works. A speaker. A microphone.

6. When sound is introduced into a simple electronic public address system, describe how sound energy is transduced from one form to another as it passes through the system.

Traditional Tools of Analog Sound Reproduction

CHAPTER 9

ELECTRONIC TOOLS

Now that something is known about how electric impulses are generated and made to behave, this chapter is a short primer of latter day standard practices for capturing and recreating music and other environmental sounds. To imprison sound and turn it into electrical impulses has been the first order of business since the late 1920s. At this time, the mechanical recording processes developed by Edison and Berliner were abandoned in favor of recording methods that "sandwiched" electrical current between the capturing mechanism (the diaphragm of the microphone) and the sound production mechanism (the **cone** of the speaker).

The placement of these electrical signals in the recording process is significant. Electrical signals can be enhanced via filters and amplifiers in order to create more realistic sound, making up for sonic deficiencies found in the recording studio or the mechanical recording system itself. These electrical signals, although replete with full spectrum audio content, are quite weak. The "missing link" then, for engineers, was to boost the energy of those weak signals so that they could be changed back into audible sound waves. In today's vernacular, this careful control of the strengths of electrical signals within the sound recording and reproduction chain is called "gain structure."

Microphones

The function of a microphone is to transduce physical vibration from the environment into electrical voltage fluctuations (much as the cochlea in the inner ear transduces vibration and encodes it into neurological signals). Not only should a microphone be capable of encoding sound signals into voltage patterns—because the audible frequency range is between 20–20,000 Hz—it would be expected that the sound system is capable of responding accurately within that frequency range. Furthermore, it should respond correctly and immediately to amplitude variations. A number of systems for transducing sound waves have been developed. Some respond more accurately than others.[1]

---

[1] *Good primers for learning about microphones (and other audio devices) are:*
White, Glenn D., The Audio Dictionary, *University of Washington Press, 1987, 290 pgs. It is suggested that the reader start by looking up "microphone" and then follow the further references that are listed.*
Huber, D.M. & Runstein, R.E., Modern Recording Techniques, *Seventh Edition, SAMS, A Division of Prentice Hall Computer Publishing, 2010.*

CONE: Speaker cone. A light material forced into motion representative of sound waves, causing changes in air pressure analogous to those sound waves.

Certain salts or crystals (piezoelectric material) when compressed, develop an electrical voltage. Some microphones make use of these crystals to create voltage fluctuations. They are aptly named **crystal microphones**. Piezoelectric material is put in a small container over which a metal disc is placed. Sound waves periodically impinge upon the disc and displace it. The disc, in turn, pushes upon the piezoelectric crystals, thereby creating voltage differences and fluctuations. The early carbon microphone developed for radio and later for audio recording, was one such device.

While crystal (and carbon) microphones reproduce frequencies fairly accurately between 100–6000 Hz, and could therefore be used for reproducing the speaking voice, their application to the accurate encoding of the remainder of the frequency spectrum (for musical recording) left much to be desired. Although once quite common (every telephone once used this type of microphone), the use of crystal microphones has declined.

In the 1930s, a second variety of microphone was developed that uses a thinner diaphragm. A coil of wire, attached to this diaphragm, is moved in and out by sound waves. As the coil passes through a magnetic field, voltage fluctuations are caused (See Figure 9-1), and sent on through a wire. This **dynamic microphone** encodes sounds over a wider frequency range and does so with more fidelity (accurate frequency and amplitude response) than do crystal microphones. Dynamic microphones are still the mainstay of today's recording studios and concert stages.

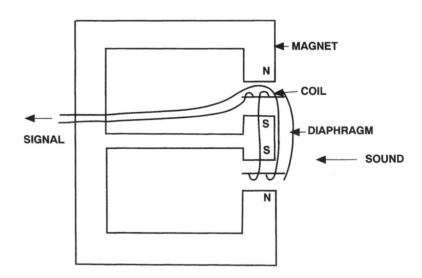

Figure 9-1. A simplified cross section of a dynamic microphone.

CRYSTAL MICROPHONES: Transducers of mechanical energy into electrical energy by the use of crystal salts or ceramics (piezoelectric material) that, when their shape is distorted by changes in air pressure on a diaphragm, produce minute voltages.

DYNAMIC MICROPHONES: Transducers using a coil of wire moving through a magnetic field to transduce mechanical energy into electrical energy.

Ribbon microphones function similarly to dynamic microphones. The diaphragm of the dynamic microphone is replaced by a small corrugated wafer housed in the field of a permanent magnet. Changes in air pressure displace the wafer within the magnetic field, producing representative changes in voltage within wires wrapped round the permanent magnetic.

The 1950s saw yet a third variety, called **condenser microphones**. They use a stretched metallic diaphragm in close proximity to a metal back plate. An electrical current is passed through both the diaphragm and the back plate. As the diaphragm moves in and out, a voltage is created by varying the distance from the diaphragm to the back plate. Condenser microphones need their own power source to polarize both the diaphragm and the back plate. Batteries and/or **phantom power** are generally used for this purpose (Figure 9-2). This type of microphone uses so little motion to generate voltages, and these voltages are of such low amplitude, that special pre-amplification is needed for the signal, even before it is sent on to the amplifier. Condenser microphones encode sounds over a very wide audio frequency range, and do so with a high degree of fidelity. The microphones found in cell phones and other small electronic devices are of this variety. Controversy over the relative merits of the choice of condenser microphones over dynamic microphones still exists, depending on one's likes and dislikes regarding the coloration; the tendency of certain microphones to influence timbre.

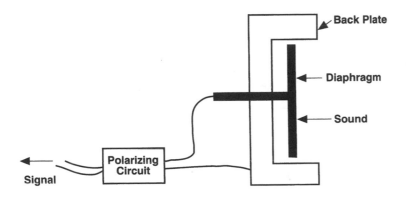

Figure 9-4. A simplified cross-section of a Condenser microphone.

A further development in microphone technology came about with the development of the **electret** microphone. An element in an electret microphone holds a permanent charge and doesn't require a polarizing voltage. Essentially, the electret is the **electrostatic** counterpart to a permanent magnet. These are sometimes called pre-polarized condenser microphones. While this development created a smaller, more sensitive microphone, the adding of an aluminum back plate was a real breakthrough. These PZM (Pressure Zone Microphones)[2] are six dB SPL more sensitive than their electret counterparts when they are placed on a floor, wall, or table top. In essence, the flat surface of the floor or wall becomes the microphone's diaphragm, and its design takes advantage of the pressure doubling when sound hits a surface and changes direction. Better fidelity (signal-to-noise ratio) is the result.

Until recently, a microphone had to be connected to an amplifier with a length of **cable** that carries the signal. The cable must have two wires to complete

---

[2] A brand name.

CONDENSER MICROPHONES: Transducers of mechanical energy that create voltage fluctuations by varying the relative positions to each other of two conductors that have been polarized using an electric current.

PHANTOM POWER: Phantom power places electrons on one side of a capacitor (a passive device that stores a small electric charge) attached to the diaphragm of a condenser microphone. The action of the diaphragm forces some of those electrons to cross from one side to the other of the capacitor, dependent on the force of the diaphragm's movement.

ELECTRET: Literally, a word made from "electricity" and "magnetism." Electret devices carry a permanent static electric charge.

CABLE: Multiple wires, each insulated from the other, that run in tandem with each other. Actually, the wires twist around each other to help cancel noise. "Shielded cable" has a network of wire mesh that runs eventually into the earth, surrounding the wires, thus preventing any influence from electrical disturbances in the environment.

a circuit. Each wire is isolated from the other by insulation material and then both are wrapped together. Good microphones use cables that have two insulated conductors that are then surrounded by a wire mesh. In this cable, the wire mesh is not part of the signal path, but acts as protection (shielding) from electronic interference in the environment that might affect the signal by its presence. This arrangement is called a "balanced line." Another configuration called "unbalanced," uses the wire mesh as one of the conductors for the signal path.

The shape of the area to which the microphone is sensitive is called the microphone's "pick-up" pattern or more correctly, its **polar pattern**. These patterns, illustrated in Figure 9-3, have been given names. Many professional recordings are done with an omnidirectional microphone so that room reverberations can be picked up along with the original sound source. However, a recording engineer, wishing to isolate one sound source within a noisy environment, would choose a microphone with a cardioid (heart shaped) polar pattern. The cardioid microphone accepts sound at the front and sides of the diaphragm while rejecting sound at the back of the diaphragm. Different recordings require different acoustical effects and recording engineers often view "the art of recording" as the selection of just the right microphone for each situation. Because subtle differences exist among microphones built by different manufacturers, personal preference and professional opinion, instead of just electronic charac-

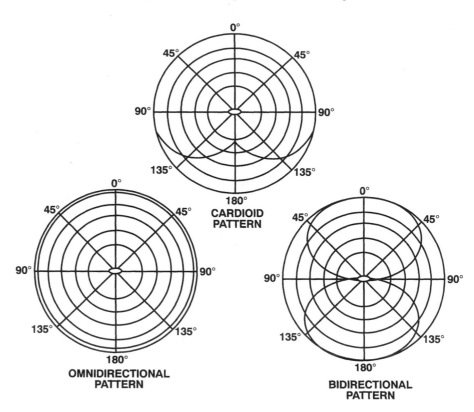

Figure 9-3. Polar patterns for different types of microphones.

POLAR PATTERN: The shape of the area in space to which a microphone is sensitive.

teristics are used to make these decisions.[3] Signals from more than one microphone may be mixed and the intensities of each signal adjusted using a microphone mixer. After mixing, the composite signal is sent to the amplifier.

There are many more types of microphones. Some of them are more common than others.

Figure 9-4. Historic microphones.

Amplifiers

Because microphones produce voltage fluctuations that are very small, it is the amplifier's function to retain the ratio of the voltage fluctuation, and increase the magnitude of the signal so the original sound can be faithfully recreated by the speaker.

The vacuum tube (sometimes called a "valve") was, until the 1960s, the heart of any amplifier. The signal coming into the tube (called the **input**) was increased from 50 to 100 times before going out again (called the **output**). An amplifier must have its own source of electrical current, which means that it must be connected to a wall socket. A large electric current could be controlled in a vacuum tube by the application of small, incoming voltages to one of its terminals. In this way, the voltages were "stepped up." The output of one tube could be directed to the input of another tube. In this "stepwise" fashion, a microphone's (or other input) signal magnitude could be considerably increased.

INPUT: The signal entering an electronic component.

OUTPUT: The signal leaving an electronic component.

---

[3] *The reader is directed to a number of reports of criteria for electronic components compiled by impartial consumer testing organizations, i.e.,* Consumer Reports. *Also, popular audio magazines often include guides to selecting components.*

Today, the **transistor** has all but replaced the vacuum tube. An unfortunate byproduct produced of vacuum tubes is heat, and heat over time can degrade the quality of electrical circuitry. Although vacuum tubes generally stepped up the incoming signal with more accuracy than transistors, they have become nearly obsolete in audio technology. Transistors emit much less heat, do not require long warm up periods, use much less power than vacuum tubes and they function almost as well. The smaller size of transistors is another factor in their favor. Transistors continue to be reduced in size as advances in micro-technology occur, thus fostering the advent of "mini" and "micro" music players, cameras, telephones, and recorders.

The amount of increase in signal size (amplification) is controlled by a dial, lever, or by pressing and holding a scrolling key located on the amplifier. This device is generally (and incorrectly) called the volume control. The correct term is the **gain** or loudness control. Its function is to regulate the magnitude of the signal sent on to the speaker.

Amplifiers are judged as to their value, by the degree to which they accurately reproduce the signal input at their output. Because no amplifier can accurately do so when it is being driven at full power, a general rule is that an amplifier should have a total potential power output that is at least one-third greater than what it will normally be called upon to use. This concept has caused audio component manufacturers to produce amplifiers of greater and greater power. However, it is not necessary to purchase "the largest" or "most powerful." It would be wise for a consumer to select an amplifier that will produce room listening volume without obvious distortion of the original sound source, and still have one-half to one-third of its power in reserve.

Found on the front of most amplifiers are controls for varying the amount of "treble" (high frequencies) and "bass" (low frequencies). These controls are positioned in the pre-amplifier stage of the amplifier, because the incoming signals are modified before they are amplified. Some manufacturers split the audio spectrum into many separate bands as portions of the frequency range and refer to these switches as equalization controls, or "graphic" EQ.[4] They are actually gain controls for separate portions of the frequency spectrum. Less expensive amplifiers combine these controls into one "tone" control. Such is the case with

TRANSISTOR: A crystalline material (usually made of germanium). It is a non-linear amplifying element used in almost all audio circuitry today. Great effort must be made to reduce distortion introduced by these devices in order to make their output linear, or like the original signal, only louder.

GAIN: The amount of increase of current allowed to flow through a circuit. Incorrectly called "volume," since that is a sensory judgment made about sounds and has little, if anything, to do with an electronic circuit.

---

[4] *A parametric equalizer, now used more commonly, adjusts the EQ around a user selected center frequency. A second control allows frequencies on either side of the center frequency to be selected for modification. A third control adjusts the amplitude of the center frequency and consequently, the degree to which the neighboring frequencies are modified.*

most small audio devices, where the treble and bass controls are coupled so that as the gain is increased in the treble range, it is simultaneously decreased in the bass range. It should be noted that many "high-end" or "state-of-the-art" audio component manufacturers suggest not using (or in some cases they do not supply) EQ controls, because recordings have already been professionally balanced throughout the frequency spectrum, and any modification of this processed signal can only be regarded as a form of distortion.

Loudspeakers

Any audio reproduction equipment can recreate sounds only as well as its speakers[5] will allow. It is the speaker that ultimately transduces voltage fluctuations (the signal) back into sound waves. One of the processes by which this is accomplished is very similar to the way a dynamic microphone operates; but the operation is reversed (Figure 9-5). This type of speaker is called, as might be expected, a dynamic speaker. Voltage fluctuations, when fed into its coil, move it back and forth within a magnetic field. The vibrations cause a paper or extremely light alloy cone (connected to the coil) to propagate vibrations into the air as sound waves. Some intercom and two-way radio systems actually use a small dynamic speaker alternately as both a microphone and a speaker. The function of the speaker/microphone is determined by a "send/receive" button.

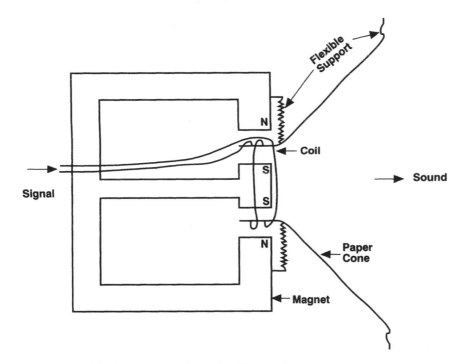

Figure 9-5. A simplified cross section of a Dynamic speaker.

---

[5] *Although originally called "loudspeakers," common usage dictates that the word "speaker" be used instead.*

119

The mission of this final link in the amplification chain is not only to reproduce the audio frequency spectrum with relationships between frequency, amplitude and complex harmonics remaining as accurate and distortion free as possible, but further, these reconstructed sounds must create a presence and ambience very much like the original surroundings. Speakers are most often combined into either **speaker units** or **speaker systems**, or even combination of both. Manufacturers build speaker units that are actually a combination of different speakers, each designed to reproduce a portion of the frequency spectrum, and all in a box called an "enclosure." Each speaker in such a unit functions best over one portion of the frequency range. In order to have the proper frequencies fed to the proper speakers, **cross-over networks** become necessary. The function of these devices is to sort the composite signal and then to send the proper frequencies to the proper speakers.

Different kinds of speakers are often used in some combination in speaker units to accomplish this task. Each has unique characteristics. "Tweeters" are the name given to speakers whose job it is to reproduce high frequency sounds. "Mid-range" speakers do just what their name implies, and "woofers" reproduce low frequencies. Sub-woofers enhance audible low frequencies; often providing the vibrations caused by ultra-low frequencies in theater settings. There are some interesting problems inherent to the faithful reproduction of an original sound source. High frequencies are quite directional and must be spread (disbursed) across the entire listening area, while low frequency sounds disburse omnidirectionally, with the whole audio range's reproduction difficulties being somewhat of a continuum. Remember also, that the lower the frequency, the more power (movement of air) it will take to reproduce the original sound. Some very original and creative thought has gone into the design of ever better speaker units and systems.

There was a time in the mid-1950s, during the infancy of the "high fidelity movement," when one could find a dynamic loudspeaker mounted on a plywood board with a circular hole cut in the board for the sound to come through. The plywood board would lean against a wall; and that was the speaker system! It did not take long for hi-fi enthusiasts to learn that enclosing their speakers in wood boxes (speaker cabinets) improved the fidelity of the sound. A speaker cabinet reinforces the middle, and especially the low frequency tones by reflecting forward the sound waves generated behind the speaker cone. Vent, or port holes were cut into the plywood speaker support. In this manner, the

SPEAKER UNIT: The combination of two or more individual tweeters, mid-range speakers or woofers in a single speaker enclosure, with the proper crossover networks.

SPEAKER SYSTEM: The combination of two or more speaker units in an audio sound system to reproduce the original sound picture.

CROSS-OVER NETWORKS: Essentially, electronic routing systems sensitive to different frequency ranges.

bass reflex speaker was developed. The term bass reflex actually refers to the kind of enclosure for the speaker. Because of the homemade nature of these early enclosures and the resulting greater reinforcement of *some* low frequencies, this type of speaker design soon became nick-named a "boom box."

Since the 1950s, two dynamic speaker designs have been marketed commercially. They are bass reflex and **air suspension speakers**. The difference is simple, but very important. The bass reflex design has a hole (called a port) in the panel to which the speakers are fastened. The air suspension variety is a sealed, airtight box with the speakers mounted on the front panel. Instead of the speaker cone being pulled back to rest by the speaker cone support (as in the bass reflex system), it is forced back to rest by the air pressure contained within the speaker cabinet. Speakers utilizing this air suspension design reproduce the frequency spectrum quite accurately, and do so in smaller cabinets than bass reflex designs.

One commercial dynamic speaker design uses a large horn shaped "woofer" mounted high in a very large corner cabinet. This speaker system is capable of extremely loud reproduction of sound, and does so quite accurately throughout the frequency spectrum. Another design uses nine, six inch diameter speakers (quite small generally, for good fidelity of sound) mounted in one cabinet, all but one of which face the wall instead of the room. Most of the sound is reflected off the hard wall surface and good sound disbursement is the result.

A very different type of speaker design is used by the "electrostatic" speaker. Its operation may be thought of as the reverse of a condenser microphone. A polarizing voltage is fed to a stretched metalized plastic membrane (a kind of plastic that conducts electricity) placed between two screens. These screens are in very close proximity to each other (Figure 9-6), and when voltage fluctuations are fed to the front and back screens ("grids"), these fluctuations move the plastic membrane to and fro, propagating sound waves.

The sound reproduction of electrostatic speakers in the middle and upper-frequencies is excellent. Because they do not reproduce low frequency sounds with much amplitude, some music listeners employ electrostatic panels for the middle and upper frequencies, but use an air suspension speaker in a separate box (called

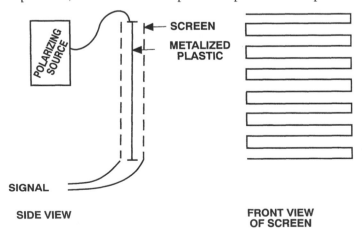

Figure 9-6. A simplified diagram of an electrostatic speaker panel.

BASS REFLEX SPEAKER: Refers to the kind of cabinet that any kind of speaker is mounted in. A speaker is mounted in the front of a box. Vent holes are also placed on the front to allow reflected and reinforced sounds from inside the box to combine with those emanating directly from the front of the speaker.

AIR SUSPENSION SPEAKER: Refers to the cabinet in which a speaker is mounted. Basically, an airtight, sealed box, that is responsible for returning the speaker cone to its neutral position using the air pressure contained within the cabinet. These are sometimes called "acoustic suspension speakers."

a subwoofer[6]) to produce and reinforce the very low frequency sounds. Interestingly, even though these systems need two separate electrostatic speakers (for stereo sound reproduction), they use only one bass speaker placed between the two electrostatic speakers. The reason that this is possible is because the lower the frequency, the more it will spread (disperse) omnidirectionally in space, and to a point, cannot be detected as originating from a particular direction by a listener.[7]

Those very small speakers found in transistor radios are different from audio system speakers because they are called upon to serve the entire frequency range. This is also true of the speakers installed on most television receivers. These tiny radio and TV speakers actually supply only the upper portion of the frequency range, and rely upon differences in the overtones of the frequencies and our ears to supply the lower frequencies.[8] The resultant sounds are not considered adequate when more accurate audio reproduction is desired.

Powered Speakers

Powered speakers include a power amplifier, carefully matched to the characteristics of a speaker system, housed within the same unit. Powered speaker systems need only to be connected to a pre-amplifier for control of input signals. Many recording studio monitoring systems and public address systems presently employ powered speaker systems.

CHANNELS OF SOUND

The advent of the "Hi-Fi" age, set at approximately 1950, was marked by the appearance of the long-playing record.[9] Recording techniques were improving, there were developments in the number, kind and quality of microphones used to record music, recording studios were built instead of having recording personnel traveling to the location of the performance, and more discrete channels of sound were created. It was a time of much change in the music business.

A Monophonic Audio System

In the previous chapter, a public address system was described using a microphone, an amplifier and a speaker. If the microphone in the system was replaced with an MP3 player, for instance, the P.A. system would instead become a music listening (or audio) system.

---

[6] *Because they reproduce only sounds between 20 and 400 hz.*

[7] *For the most up-to-date information concerning the design and configuration of speakers (or for any audio component, for that matter), one need go only as far as the nearest audio components retail outlet. Salespeople are happy to discuss design, response, endurance, and other factors relating to the components that they sell. The web is another source of design and performance data.*

[8] *See Chapter 4: "residue effect."*

[9] *Records before the dawn of the hi-fi age were spun or turned at 78 revolutions per minute. The "new" records were played at either 45 rpm (for "popular music") or at 33⅓ rpm for music that was lengthier. One side of a long-playing record (LP) played back approximately twenty minutes of music.*

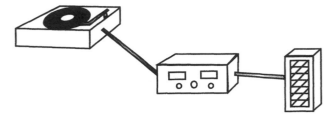

Figure 9-7. A monophonic sound system.

An audio system then, is a series of electrical components whose function is to retrieve sounds that have either been stored or broadcast, to amplify them, and then to transduce these signals back into the original sounds. Not only can a radio be used as the first component in such an audio system, the initial component may be a CD, MP3, or a DVD player, a radio, or any audio delivery system. With any one of these components linked by cable to an amplifier and a single speaker, a monophonic audio reproduction system is the result.

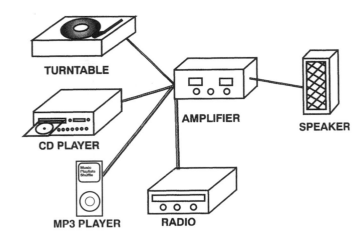

Figure 9-8. Component possibilities in an audio system

A Stereophonic Audio System

Essentially, stereophonic sound is produced by using two separate monophonic sound systems in conjunction with each other. When sounds are recorded, two separate microphones are set somewhat apart from each other, in front of, but to the left and to the right of the sound source. Each microphone is connected to a separate amplifier. Sounds from each channel are stored individually, on the same medium, and later simultaneously played back through two separate speakers or speaker systems.[10] The resultant two channels of cross linked sound produce a stereophonic audio image, or sound that has the minute

---

[10] *In actuality, an almost unlimited number of separate channels of sound may be recorded, stored on separate "tracks," and later "mixed down" to stereo's two channels.*

delays, intensity changes and phasing differences originally detected by the microphones at the sound's source. Such sounds, when compared with monophonic sounds, are said to have "depth." Stereo amplifiers are generally what are available (they are really two amplifiers in one box, sharing a power supply) in today's audio marketplace.[11] However, 5.1 and other surround sound systems have replaced stereo imaging, most often in the multimedia, video gaming, and home theater markets.

Any design or electrical problems inherent in monophonic sound are essentially the same for stereophonic reproduction; but with stereo there is a further problem. Not only is the accurate reproduction of frequencies and amplitudes required, but distortions and non-linearities within the sound field (and there are still many), must be quite similar in both channels of stereo sound. Listeners are less likely to notice variations in reproduction if both channels produce the same deviations from the original sound. Manufacturers of stereophonic equipment have been careful, in most cases, to match the electronic components used to build each channel, thus reducing this problem.

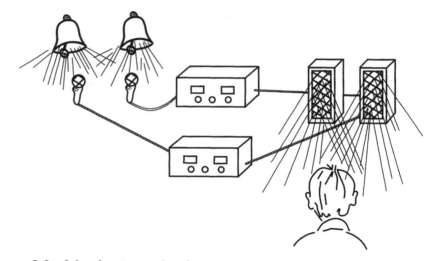

Figure 9-9. A basic stereophonic system.

More Channels of Sound

What was once called quadraphonic (four channel) sound has recently been reintroduced and is now being called "surround sound," or "5.1 audio."[12] Not only are multiple microphones used in the recording process, but there are additional microphones placed at varying distances from the sound source and sent to additional channels. As would be expected, delays in the sound's travel are recorded, as well as echoes and the acoustic characteristics of the concert hall or recording studio. These ambient acoustic characteristics are detected

---

[11] *Although, with the advent of "surround sound," "pro-logic" sound and "THX" sound for home theaters, more and more channels of sound are being created for home use.*

[12] *The 5 represents a left, center and right speaker in front, and a left and right rear speaker. The .1 represents a subwoofer.*

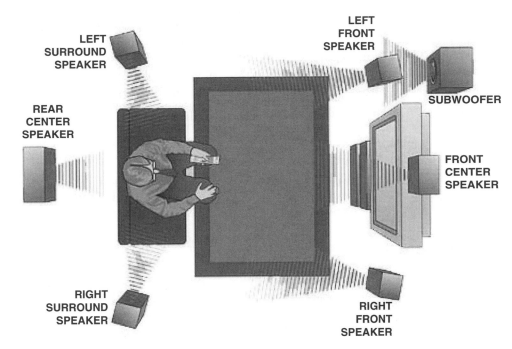

LEFT SURROUND SPEAKER

REAR CENTER SPEAKER

RIGHT SURROUND SPEAKER

LEFT FRONT SPEAKER

SUBWOOFER

FRONT CENTER SPEAKER

RIGHT FRONT SPEAKER

Figure 9-10. A home theater system.

and played back through an array of speakers placed on all sides of (surrounding) the listener. The addition of the rear speakers give an added feeling of "depth" or "realism" to the listener since the aural environment that is created by multiple speakers further recreates the acoustical characteristics of the area in which the sounds were recorded. The combination of sound delays, variations in intensity of sound and phasing differences from one set of speakers to the other are detectable to our binaural hearing apparatus. Again, arguments ensue among listeners as to whether excellent, proven, stereo equipment or the latest surround sound system is the better sound reproducing system.[13]

OTHER ADVANCES IN AUDIO REPRODUCTION

High fidelity is a term that was used by the audio industry from the 1950s through the early 1980s to describe rather sophisticated electronic sound equipment that reproduced a frequency range from about 30 Hz to 15,000 Hz; and did so with an amplitude error of less than two decibels in either direction (sometimes written +/- 2 dB). Since then, sound reproducing equipment has been improving, and of course, has steadily increased in popularity. There have been a number of technological advances making audio's "state-of-the-art" a seemingly ever improving continuum. Today's audio reproduction equipment easily surpasses those early standards, and distortion figures are now reported by manufacturers in tenths and hundredths of one percent!

---

[13] *It is the practice of movie studios to actually create some of the "exotic" sounds in today's movies. These are not "recreated sounds," but actually synthesized and carefully placed spatially within the audio environment. Thus, "fantasy events" can be manufactured using both sound synthesis and Foley sound (actual sounds manufactured in a laboratory.)*

The development of the transistor was one such improvement. The advent of printed circuitry is another. Instead of making electrical connections between various components with metal wire, as was the practice in the past, metal imprints are made on the soft surface of a composition board. Not only can complicated circuitry be accomplished in this manner without a great deal of wiring, but through improved printed circuitry techniques, additional miniaturization has been made possible. By plugging transistors and other electrical parts (chips and microchips[14]) into a printed circuit, one stage of an electrical component may be constructed. Many such circuits can then be connected to each other, thereby constructing a complete electronic component. Through these developments and others, the efficiency, size and life of electronic audio equipment has been steadily improving.

Some of today's audio systems employ wireless technology. Audio signals, encoded in radio signals, are broadcast to amplification systems housed in speaker cabinets or ear pieces (such as headphones and "ear buds") thus negating the need for "hard wiring." Many of these systems encode digitized audio in FM radio signals with very limited broadcast range. Newer technologies, such as "Bluetooth" and "Wi-Fi" use sophisticated broadcast technologies that function over short distances on radio frequency bands available world-wide. These systems are able to "weave" their broadcast frequencies around other frequencies so they avoid being interfered with by stronger radio signals. Other advances in audio technology include increased microphone and amplifier sensitivity so extremely high and extremely low frequencies can be captured, stored, and faithfully reproduced.

DISCUSSION QUESTIONS FOR CHAPTER NINE

1. Describe how electric current can cause the physical movement of a magnet. How is this principle applied to sound systems?

2. How do microphones function? Name two varieties and describe how they transduce sound.

3. Why is "volume control" not a good label for the control that regulates the magnitude of the signal sent from the amplifier?

4. What is meant by the term "high fidelity?"

5. Describe how "Stereo" sound reproduction differs from "Monophonic" sound. Describe the resultant differences both physically and psychologically.

---

[14] *Chips and microchips are silica derivatives that function as cross-over networks, filter signals, and store memory for audio components.*

Analog Storage of Music

CHAPTER 10

THE PHONODISK

Well over a century ago, Thomas A. Edison invented a method of recording sounds on a grooved cylinder covered with tin foil.[1] A metal stylus mounted on a thin diaphragm and attached to a large horn that served as a primitive microphone was brought into contact with the tin-foil-covered rotating cylinder. Acoustical vibrations (air pressure variations), made by the voice, were converted to mechanical vibrations at the stylus, and deformed the tin foil in the pattern of the mechanical vibration. When the stylus retraced its original cut into the tin foil, the voice was mechanically reproduced and amplified through the horn (Figure 10-1).

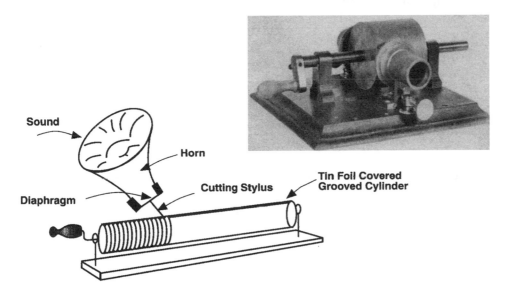

Figure 10-1. Mechanical recording apparatus.

This **analog** recording process was subsequently improved by using flat disks made of wax, into which an impression of mechanical vibration from the recording horn was cut. Using the wax disk as a mold, a harder "master" disk was created, and from it hard rubber copies could be pressed. These were sold commercially as phonograph records. Later, they were simply called "records."

> **ANALOG: The recording and playing of sounds in real time. The flow of information is continuous.**

---

[1] Culver, Charles A., Musical Acoustics, (New York: McGraw-Hill Book Company, 1956), p. 261.

There were severe fidelity limitations inherent in this early mechanical (non-electrical) recording process. Higher frequencies and most overtones were reduced or eliminated entirely, and the sound intensity required to noticeably move the recording stylus was very large. For playback on the mechanical "talking machine," the hard, sharp cutting stylus, that originally cut the grooves, was replaced with a blunt, steel "needle" that followed the wavy grooves of the record and reproduced the vibrations. Because of the relatively wide space taken by these wavy grooves, approximately four minutes of recording per side was available on a ten-inch-in-diameter, hard rubber record disk. These disks were recorded and played back at 78 revolutions per minute (rpm). This speed was necessary to gain enough fidelity to be practical. The speed allowed a complex waveform to be recorded and played back over a longer distance on the disk, thus lessening the tendency for one wave peak to interfere with its neighboring amplitude peak. Yet, speed also generated a fair amount of centrifugal force creating the tendency for the needle to want to leave the groove. Weight was needed to keep the stylus in the record groove, and while it did that well, the consequent increase in friction caused lots of wear to both record and needle.

In spite of the fact that recorded music compositions had to be interrupted every four minutes so that the disk could be changed; and in spite of frequency limitations, relatively small amplitude changes, and the great amount of record and needle wear, the music of some of the world's most renown singers, instrumentalists, and orchestras of the early twentieth century has been preserved using this early mechanical method of recording sounds.

With the invention and subsequent improvement of the vacuum tube, electronic amplification of musical sounds became feasible. Mechanical energy could be transduced, amplified and transduced again at greater energy levels; and done so with more accurate reproduction of frequency and amplitude ranges. In the late 1940s, as improvements were made in the designs and operation of microphones, amplifiers and record cutters, high fidelity recordings became possible. Records could be rotated at 33-1/3 rpm and up to thirty minutes or more of material could be recorded on one side of a twelve inch in diameter vinyl plastic disk.

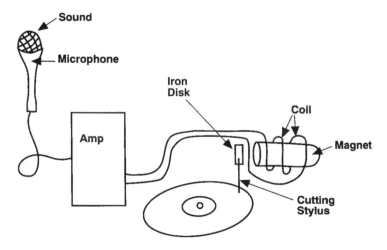

Figure 10-2. Simplified electronic method of recording on a disk.

An electrical process called "equalization," was added to the recording process to change the amplitude of different frequencies within the recorded signal.[2] This was done so all frequencies would create nearly the same amount of stylus deflection. The groove width was narrowed for low frequencies and high frequencies were made to cut a wider path into the groove. Using this method, two problems associated with frequency were overcome when recording to disk. This process kept the bass frequencies from taking up so much groove width, thus conserving record space; and treble frequencies were made to displace just enough to overcome random noise occurring naturally on the vinyl record disk. All record playback equipment came equipped with this standardized set of "correcting" electrical circuits in the **pre-amplifier** that again amplified according to the same pattern. This "equalized" the signal before it reached the main amplifier.[3] Electronic equalizing of amplitudes on records was done according to frequency; i.e., the lower the frequency, the more the sound's amplitude was diminished during the recording process, and the more it must again be amplified upon playback; and conversely with high frequencies. The resultant pre-amplified signal became a very close approximation of the original signal, yet saved record space and overcame noise problems.

Stereophonic records use the two sides of the record groove. One channel of sound is recorded on the "inside" of the groove, while the other channel is recorded on the "outside." Stereophonic cartridges are designed so that displacement of the stylus in different directions will not only transduce the signal, but will also transmit each stereophonic signal to the proper channel (See Figure 10-3). Using Figure 10-3, and Figure 10-4, an understanding can be gained of how two channels of sound are recorded using one stylus. To reproduce the original effect during playback, it is important that the proper channel be fed to the proper speaker, so the reproduced sounds approximate the same spatial relationships that were present during the recording process.

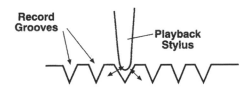

Figure 10-3. Stylus displacement in the stereo playback of record disks.

Phonographs

The term "phonograph" means the physical configurations within the record groove. The record groove is a graphic representation of sound. Phonographs, or

---

[2] *Villchur, Edgar,* Reproduction of Sound, *(New York: Dover Publications, 1965).*

[3] *For this reason, no other input device will sound correct if connected to the "phono" input of an amplifier.*

PRE-AMPLIFIER: Certain frequency and amplitude considerations necessitate that output signals from records, tapes and microphones be processed (the increasing and subsequent decreasing of certain frequency and amplitude ranges) to deliver a signal to the amplifier that will accurately reproduce the original sound. The pre-amplifier performs this processing.

record players are names given to the electronic component that plays records. For a while, they were self-contained units with their own turntable, amplifier and speaker system. A separate record playing unit is called a turntable; yet this label and description is too simplistic. The actual turntable is that portion of the component upon which the record is placed, then rotated. Also needed are a phono-stylus, a phono cartridge and a tone arm.

Styli

The stylus (it was called the phonograph needle) is the component that fits into and rides in the record's groove (each side of a record has only one inwardly spiraling groove). The tip of the stylus is made of diamond or an extremely hard synthetic material because it is subjected to almost constant friction and consequently, wear. Two shapes have been extensively used for styli. The conical shape is probably more traditional, and when magnified, looks like the point or tip on an ice cream cone. However, the elliptical shape is thought by some to be more sensitive to the sides of the record grooves (on which are encoded the patterns of sound's vibrations). The shape of an elliptical stylus might be likened to the tip of an ice cream cone that has been pinched. Whichever shaped stylus is used is mounted in an elastic mounting housed in the phono cartridge.

Phono Cartridges

Phono cartridges are transducers of the stylus' vibration. Less expensive models are called ceramic or crystal cartridges because they use piezoelectric crystals to generate voltage as the stylus displaces them, much in the same manner as a crystal microphone operates. Magnetic cartridges (functioning somewhat like dynamic microphones) depend upon the stylus to move a coil through a magnetic field as in Figure 10-4; or to move a magnet in the proximity of a coil. The voltage fluctuations caused by such movement are, as in the case of the microphone, very weak. Wires from the cartridge run through the tone arm and eventually to the amplifier, where the signal is increased in strength and sent on to the speaker.

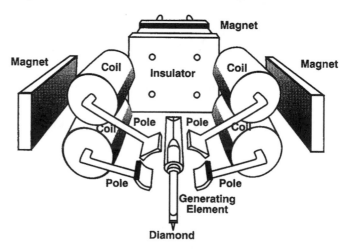

Figure 10-4. One design of a magnetic cartridge.

Tone Arms

The stylus and cartridge are mounted on one end of a tone arm. The other end of the arm is mounted next to the turntable on a pivot. The function of this unit is to move the cartridge and stylus across the record toward its center, as the stylus moves through the record's groove. Through the history of recording, the tone arm has been the subject of a great deal of research. If the stylus is left to be pulled through the groove of a record while bearing the weight of the cartridge and the tone arm, a great deal of wear due to friction occurs. To avoid such wear, tone arms have been designed with a counterbalance (another weight at the opposite end of the arm) so that minimum "tracking force" is exerted. By using counterbalancing devices, a magnetic cartridge, if sensitive enough, can exert less than one gram of pressure on a record groove while transducing the signal accurately. This is considerably less than the actual combined weight of a tone arm and cartridge. Most ceramic cartridges must track at a higher tracking force, (more weight upon the record) and consequently, generate proportionately greater friction, and wear in the record groove.

To prevent wear to the side of the record groove as the stylus is pulled through the groove to the center of the record, various "antiskating" devices have been tried. Many tone arms in the past have made use of complex weights, angled counterbalances, levers and/or gears.

Turntables

A turntable's function is very simple. It makes the record turn. However, this is not quite as uncomplicated a process as it seems. Power fluctuations encountered when other appliances run on the same electrical circuit can affect (slow) the speed of a turntable's rotation. The subsequent slowing of a record lowers the pitch and changes the timbre of whatever is being played and can be quite musically disturbing. A special kind of motor was developed and marketed in the early 1960s that maintained a steady speed. The hysteresis-synchronous motor derives its speed from the regular alternations of household current, rather than depending upon the current's magnitude. Also, heavy turntables, once they achieve their optimum speed, rotate at a more constant speed than light-weight ones. Many mechanisms have been developed using either a belt, a rubber drive wheel, or a motor that is directly coupled to the platter and made to turn at the proper speed (direct drive). Each system strives for the same result—steady rotation of the record. The speed for long playing recordings was internationally standardized at 33-1/3 rpm (revolutions per minute). Adequate sound reproduction can be achieved, only if the turntable could be made to maintain that constant speed.

For nearly sixty years the record player and its companion, the long playing record were the preferred choice for storing and playing music. By combining the optimum design characteristics of a good stylus, cartridge, tone arm and turntable, the vibrations of the stylus could quite accurately encode physical variations on the walls of the record groove into voltage fluctuations, with a minimum of wear to the record. Sixty years of development in this area resulted in very credible sonic reproduction. These signals were sent on to the amplifier to be increased in amplitude so the speaker or speaker system could transform the electrical signals into sound. It must be said that there are still audiophiles who swear that vinyl recordings translate sonics better than digital recordings do.

MAGNETIC TAPE

Late in the 19th century Valdemar Poulson introduced the "Telegraphone," a machine that recorded an audio signal magnetically on wire. Although the device received recognition at the Paris World Exhibition of 1900, it was commercially devoid of purpose and only experimental in nature. The invention of the microphone and amplifier, necessary for amplifying and recording audible sound, were decades away.[4] In the late 1920s, it was discovered that magnetic signals could be encoded on a long strip of paper coated with iron particles.[5] Later, this same process was again tried with steel wire, because it was less likely to break. Variations in the magnetic field of a magnet were produced by connecting a microphone to a wire coil around a magnet. By passing the wire through this varying magnetic field, areas of magnetic intensity could be recorded on the moving steel. When the wire was re-spooled and played back over the magnet and coil that had now been connected to a telephone receiver, the result was a reasonable facsimile of the sounds that had been recorded.

In the early 1950s the steel wire was permanently replaced by magnetic recording tape; a thin ribbon of plastic, coated with iron oxide or chromium particles. Plastics had recently been developed that were now strong enough to not break or stretch significantly when the tape was stopped from the fast forward or rewind speeds. The oxide particles bonded to the inside of this plastic tape were essentially a source of millions of permanent magnets, their poles in random patterns. Placing the oxide coated tape within a magnetic field forces the oxide particles to become polarized, aligning north and south magnetic poles. In essence, each molecule of iron oxide is itself, a tiny permanent magnet. These polar patterns were retained on the oxide coated tape. Recording was accomplished by spooling magnetic tape, and drawing it, at a constant speed, across an **electro-magnet** whose field intensity changed according to voltage fluctuations dictated by the electrical output of a microphone. This forced the oxide particles to align their magnetic poles in patterns that represent (are analogous to) the electrical output of the microphone. Playback was accomplished by re-spooling

---

ELECTRO-MAGNET: A magnet created by the induction of an electrical flow through iron.

[4] *Gronow, Pekka & Ilpo Saunio. An International History of the Recording Industry.* Cassell Books, London, 1999. p. 97.

[5] *Strangely, it was gold-tipped cigarettes that created the situation for the invention of the tape recorder. In the 1920s, it was the fashion for ladies to smoke gold-tipped cigarettes. At the factory, each had to be dipped in a gold-colored powder. Those who gathered up the cigarettes and packed them had to be careful to pack them all with the gold end up. A machine was developed to magnetically scan the packs to "see" if all the cigarettes were packed properly. Data were stored on ferrous oxide-coated magnetic tape so that a record of mistakes could be kept. Watching this system work one day, its inventor came upon the idea of speeding up the tape and trying to record sound vibrations. There's more to the story, but it worked, and the rest, as they say, is history.*

the tape, and again drawing it across the electro-magnet. This time the varying intensity of the magnetism stored on the tape varied the magnetic field of the electromagnet (the playback head). These field fluctuations were encoded as voltage fluctuations in the coil, sent to an amplifier where their magnitude was increased many hundreds of times, and then sent on to a speaker. By subjecting the recorded (magnetized) tape to a magnetic field of high frequency alternating current, the patterns of magnetism were randomized and the tape could be "erased" of its signal and thereby could again be made ready for re-recording.

Magnetic tape has been a very versatile sound recording development both in the recording industry and in home sound systems. Until the digital recording process was developed in the 1980s (the subject of Chapter 11), it was the practice of recording studios making commercial disk recordings, to record first on magnetic tape, then to transfer this recorded signal to disks. This process of analog tape recording was the practice for more than 60 years of our recent music history. Magnetic tapes could be edited by physically cutting out one section of tape and splicing in a new section. Using this process, the very best from each recording session could be edited into a final version, which made it possible to sometimes get a musically better performance than any single live performance. Later, editing was accomplished electronically, when it became the practice of recording studios to record on more than one track at a time.

Magnetic tapes have been manufactured in various thicknesses. The thinner the tape, the more tape that fits on a spool and the longer the recording time that is possible. Unfortunately, it is also true that the thinner the tape, the thinner the plastic backing and oxide coating. If tapes are very thin, and have been stored for a long time, one layer tends to imprint its magnetic "message" upon the adjacent layer. In playback, this **print through** can be heard softly along with the original recorded signal. Tape thicknesses are measured in mils (one thousandth of an inch). Generally, if a tape was to be stored for any period of time, 1 mil tape was too thin. One and one-half mil seemed to be an acceptable tape thickness for storage of recorded signals.

Metal oxides are also graded according to their composition and how fine the particles of oxide are. The finer the oxide coating, the more particles of oxide there were, and the more signal could be stored on the tape. Also, finer oxides result ultimately in less wear to the magnetic **tape head**. Until the advent of the digital age, the grade of tape to be used was best chosen by pre-determining the frequency and amplitude range and the quality of the material to be recorded. If excellent high fidelity playback was required, a good tape grade was chosen. If the frequency and amplitude range of speech was all that was required, a lower grade sufficed. If tapes were to be played on small portable machines without full frequency range playback, a lower grade of tape was also sufficient.

One notable development in tape technology was the use of chromium dioxide instead of iron oxide particles as the coating of magnetic tape. Chromium dioxide was manufactured in only one grade, and had several advantages over iron oxide. It permitted better storage of high frequencies, allowed a more

PRINT THROUGH: Adjacent layers of spooled magnetic tape, if too thin, may have the magnetic imprint of one layer transferred to the adjacent layer, called print through. Also, if one groove on a record lies too close to an adjacent groove, the phono stylus may receive a portion of the signal from the adjacent groove. On records, this is referred to as "pre-groove echo."

TAPE HEAD: A magnet across which the magnetic tape is pulled. Three functions are performed by tape heads: 1) erasing previous magnetic imprints, 2) recording, and 3) playing back.

133

consistent coating, and permitted less tape noise. Because chromium dioxide tapes were harder to erase, tape machines had to be designed specifically for their use. Tape "drop-outs" were the nemesis of the recording industry. If there was a portion of tape that either did not have a coating or had a coating that was too thin, damaged, or the coating was insensitive to magnetic change, no signal was recorded on that portion of the tape. In fact, in the early 1950s, this was a very difficult problem to solve. If, for instance, a major symphony were assembled to make a recording, a single drop-out on the recorded master tape could end up costing the recording company more money than the record could be expected to finally recover in sales.

Some plastic tape was also subject to stretching, which in essence, on playback, placed a set number of cycles per second of frequency along a greater distance of tape, thus creating momentary drops in pitch. While in most instances this would be considered highly undesirable, some musicians, especially in the commercial and experimental realms, explored the sonic possibilities of this anomaly, and developed an audio effect called "flanging," to simulate this occurrence.

Today, audio and video tapes are much improved. All tape begins life as a ribbon of Mylar film. The backing is coated with a variety of metal materials onto which images and sounds are recorded when the metal particles are magnetized. Another development placed a carbon coating on the back of the tape. This helped to strengthen the tape, and because carbon can function as a lubricant, reduced friction and wear as the tape passed through the transport mechanism. Metal Evaporated (ME) tape contains metal particles bound to the polyester film by a special evaporation process. Metal Particle (MP) tape is produced by much the same process but the film is coated with small metal particles instead of oxides. There are fewer dropouts and the tapes are sturdier, smoother and more consistent.

Tape Heads

Three separate functions were accomplished by tape heads: 1) erasing a recorded signal, 2) recording an audio signal, and 3) playing back the recorded signal. All tape recorders have an **erase head**. Its requirements were quite different from either of the other two functions. By drawing the magnetic tape through a high intensity magnetic field of alternating current, the magnetic patterns on the tape were re-randomized and the recorded signal erased. Unfortunately, this process was never absolutely complete, since the coating was not demagnetized but rather, randomly remagnetized. Even though the general effect of these random magnetizations was to cancel each other out, some currents could always be measured at a given moment. When the tape passed the playback head, these currents were heard as **tape noise**. Its sound was much like white noise. An interesting method of reducing this noise is discussed later in this chapter.

Because the functions of the **playback** and **record heads** are similar in operation, some tape machines used just one head to accomplish both tasks. Other, more versatile machines used separate record and playback heads.

ERASE HEAD: The tape head that precedes the record head to "erase" any signal previously recorded on the magnetic tape. Tapes are "erased" by high frequency alternating current that randomize the magnetic patterns on the tape.

TAPE NOISE (tape hiss): White noise created by the magnetized, randomized, iron oxide particles on magnetic tape. Full tape erasure cannot be obtained because as the tape passes the head at any given moment, some randomized magnetized particles are in alignment with the playback head. The random voltage fluctuation produced by these particles passing the tape head produce noise. This noise limits how small a signal's amplitude may be recorded.

PLAYBACK HEAD: The tape head that sends a signal to the amplifier by varying its magnetic field in accordance with a recorded signal that is passed across its gap on tape.

RECORD HEAD: The tape head that receives a signal from an amplifier and produces variations in its magnetic field, thus magnetizing a portion of the oxide coating on the recording tape as it passes across its gap.

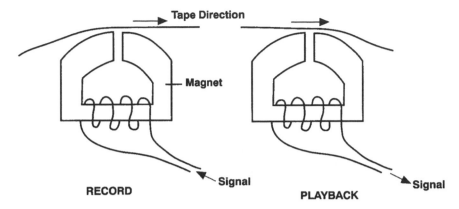

Figure 10-5. A simplified side view of a single tape head in both record and playback operation.

The amount of tape surface in contact with the record head, the speed of the tape across the head, and the gap in the magnet of the record head have a direct bearing upon the range of frequencies that can be recorded. Since recording the signal (magnetization) of the tape depends upon fluctuating alternating current (in essence, the signal) flowing ultimately to the magnetic tape, the tape has to be moved rapidly enough across the record head gap so that one-half a cycle of current is not negated by the second half of the same cycle being imprinted over it. These alternations of current flow happen at the same rate as the frequency of the sound being recorded. The speed of the tape, the width of the record head gap, and the amount of oxide were all factors in the recording of a signal on magnetic tape. Therefore, the faster the tape speed, the narrower the gap, and the finer the oxide, the better the fidelity of the recorded signal. Tape speeds were standardized at 1-7/8 inches per second (ips), 3-3/4 ips, 7-1/2 ips, 15 ips and 30 ips. Most commercial recording companies used 30 ips to record their master tapes. Cassette recorders used a speed of 1-7/8 ips.[6]

Tape Formats

At the beginning of the Twenty-first century, when digital recorders made these analog machines obsolete, most small "portable" tape machines recorded and played back in stereo. But until the mid 1970s these portable machines were only capable of recording monophonically (one channel sound). Those early tape heads were designed so that only one-half the tape was recorded as the tape passed the record head. When the tape had been completely wound onto the take up spool, the tape could be turned over, and recorded on the other half (Figure 10-6).

---

[6] *The 8-track cartridge was popular for a time. These were almost exclusively sold pre-recorded. Their use peaked in the late 1960s.*

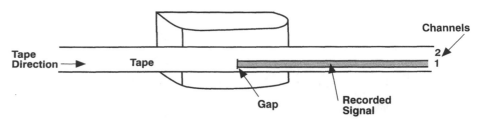

Figure 10-6. A view of a monophonic tape head recording a signal.

Stereo tape recorders marketed for home use had four **tracks** or recording paths; two for stereo reproduction while the tape ran in one direction and two for the other direction (Figure 10-7). As the tape passed the stereo record head, sections 1 and 3 of the magnetic tape were recorded. When the tape was turned over, sections 2 and 4 were in contact with the magnetically sensitive area of the record head. These tape heads were known as **quarter track heads** because each magnetically sensitive area of the tape head recorded 1/4 of the tape.

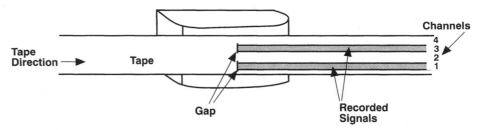

Figure 10-7. A view of a quarter track tape head recording a stereophonic signal.

Before the practice of "multi-tracking" was developed, tape heads on tape machines used for studio recording often used one-half the record head for recording one channel and the other half to record channel two; both side-by-side. This allowed more iron oxide to be in contact with those early tape heads. More signal could be recorded on the tape. Tapes for professional use were made wider and wider in a quest to record with the best fidelity possible. Commercial recorders began with 1/2 inch wide tapes that ran in one direction, then moved to 1, then 2-inch tape widths. Prior to the digital recording revolution, professional studios utilized 2-inch wide, 48 track recording tape, sometimes syncing two recording machines together, so that 96 audio tracks could be recorded simultaneously. One track was often dedicated to what was known as a "click track," or a mechanically produced beat that the musicians could hear as they played. Some designs required the placement of a synchronizing tone on one machine. The speed of the motor of a second tape machine was linked to the synchronizing tone so that variations in the master machine were replicated in the slaved machine.

It was the practice to have musicians come to the studio, record background for a song, and then a solo singer or performer could play as many times as was necessary for a "perfect" performance. Popular music moved in that direction, while most classical orchestras still preferred "live" recording. Today, SMPTE[7]

---

[7] *The acronym SMPTE stands for the Society of Motion Picture and Television Engineers.*

TRACK: The path that is recorded on magnetic tape.

QUARTER TRACK HEAD: Tape heads that produce four separate tracks. In most quarter track machines, tracks 1 and 3 are played while the tape runs forward, and when the tape's direction is reversed, tracks 2 and 4 may be played. However, a machine may be configured so that all four tracks are used in the same direction simultaneously.

digital timing code, generated by a "word clock" (a timing device used to link a number of machines together in time), is often used so that electronic instruments can take their timing from it, and video artists can synchronize their works to it.

Noise Reduction

As discussed earlier, one problem plaguing high quality tape recording had been the noise of randomized magnetic iron oxide particles. This sound, consisting mainly of high frequency white noise, could be heard by placing a previously erased tape on a tape recorder and playing it. While the loudness level of the noise was not great, it was clearly audible if the gain control was set at the same level at which pre-recorded tapes were played back. The difference between this noise level and the level of any recorded signal is called the **signal-to-noise ratio**. Better and better oxides were developed to allow a signal to be recorded at higher relative levels, thus increasing the tape's signal-to-noise ratio. As would be expected, the speed at which a tape passes the record head also has a great deal to do with the signal-to-noise ratio. Faster tape speeds allow more signal to be placed on the tape, thus increasing the signal-to-noise ratio, or reducing background hissing.

This noise, sometimes called "tape hiss," was traditionally a crucial factor in re-recording. Every time a tape recording was re-recorded, the noise from the first generation tape was re-recorded onto the second generation, whose own tape noise was being recorded. The signal remained at one level, but the noise was incrementally increased.

An ingenious invention to combat this problem was the Dolby noise reduction system.[8] The record and playback signals, when processed by Dolby circuitry, greatly improved the signal-to-noise ratio. The noise reduction system accepts a signal from a microphone, a tape machine or a turntable, and proportionally increases the amplitude of the signal according to its frequency. The higher the frequency and the lower the amplitude of the signal, the greater the amplitude is increased by the Dolby circuitry. This processed signal is sent to the record head, and recorded on the magnetic tape. When the Dolby tape is played back, the signal goes from the playback head to the noise reduction system, where the signal is reprocessed in reverse, and then on to the amplifier. By so doing, the high frequency tape hiss (noise) is reduced. This process was a much better way of reducing the tape noise than high frequency filters (that are available on some amplifiers) because by filtering that frequency range where tape noise occurs, all signals in that range are suppressed, even those that are a part of the recorded signal.

Originally, circuitry was built into all tape recorders to equalize the inherent losses of high frequencies. In order to gain favorable frequency response and adequate signal-to-noise ratio, some frequencies were amplified more than others, and balance was again restored to the signal at the amplifier. This process was known as **equalization**. Until about 1965, European tape equalization was accomplished by amplifying a slightly different frequency range than that amplified

SIGNAL-TO-NOISE RATIO: The amount of amplitude difference between the level of noise on a tape, and the recorded signal. The greater the signal-to-noise ratio, the better.

EQUALIZATION: The standard that is used for circuitry in tape machines to increase and subsequently decrease the amplitude of certain frequencies in order to restore inherent frequency losses in tape recording.

---

[8] *Named after Ray Dolby, its inventor.*

by the equalization process used in the United States. Therefore, when played back on American machines, tapes recorded on European tape recorders would not give true reproductions of the signal stored on the tape. After a time, European manufacturers began using American equalization standards.

During the tape recording process, a **Bias Current** of 100,000 Hz or more is usually recorded onto the tape along with the audio signal. Bias currents, well above the audible frequency range of human hearing, improve the signal saturation quality of the tape, producing a recording with greater audio clarity. The bias current has the effect of helping to remove any previous signal on the tape that might be summed with the new signal being recorded. It also pushes the amplitudes of some frequencies to levels that the tape is better able to record.

TAPE MACHINES

There are many kinds of tape machines. Generally, they may be grouped into two main categories; tape decks and tape recorders. Tape decks have no amplifier or speaker system contained in the unit, while tape recorders do. Each has advantages, depending upon the kind of use the machine will be called upon to perform.

All tape machines needed one or more motors to wind and rewind the tape. They also needed a system for the smooth stopping of reels of tape, once they had been set in motion, so that the tape either did not continue to unwind, or break. Shielded motors that did not record their noise on tapes and braking systems that did not damage the tape when the machine was stopped, could be found on all machines.

Controls

Tape machines had to perform a number of functions. Once a tape was placed upon the deck, it was possible to 1) "play" it, 2) "record" on it, 3) wind the tape "fast forward," 4) "rewind" the tape, 5) or "stop." There were five controls to activate the proper motors, circuits and brake systems as needed. The switches for each of these functions were located on the fronts of the machines.

Meters to indicate the strength or amplitude of the signal being recorded were included on many tape recorders. A signal recorded at too low a level would allow a certain portion of the playback to be masked by tape noise. If the signal was recorded at too high a level, the iron oxide coating on the tape became "saturated" and signal distortion resulted. For these reasons, meters were very useful for monitoring the signal's strength when recording. In recording studio jargon, adjusting the amplitude of the audio signal so that distortion is avoided was called controlling "headroom."

Many smaller tape recorders and "micro recorders" had a circuit called **automatic gain control (AGC)**. This circuitry automatically boosted the level of signals at low amplitudes, and reduced the amplitude of very loud sounds, thus

BIAS CURRENT: Inaudible ultra high frequencies introduced to the tape recording process to improve the fidelity of problematic audible frequencies and amplitudes usually masked by tape noise, an inherent condition of magnetic recording tape.

AUTOMATIC GAIN CONTROL: Circuitry added to smaller tape recorders that automatically boosts an audio signal if it is below a certain pre-specified level, or automatically lowers it if the signal is too high.

preventing record level "mistakes." Tape machines used for recording high fidelity sounds did not use this AGC circuitry because a more realistic recording of a full range of amplitudes was, of course, preferred.

The recording tape—essentially a permanent magnet—passing through the transport mechanism of a tape machine, causes the metal tape guides and other metal parts to slowly become magnetized. This magnetic energy can degrade the quality of subsequent recordings. It is essential that the metal parts of a tape machine, especially near the record and playback heads, be demagnetized. This is most often accomplished with a small hand-held electrical coil placed in the vicinity of the magnetized parts, through which 110 volts (household current) are passing. Similar to the way tape is erased, the magnetic patterns that have developed on the tape machine are re-randomized.

Musical Effects Before Digital Recording

Many reel-to-reel recorders had features that made it possible to achieve certain tape recording "effects." Because tape speeds are multiples of 2 (i.e., 3-3/4 and 7-1/2), or at a ratio of 2:1, by recording a signal at one speed, and playing it back at a faster or slower speed, the subsequent frequency changes are in octaves. Of course, the tempo was then also increased or decreased by the same factor.

Stereophonic tape machines that had a separate "record" control switch for each channel, could achieve an effect known as "sound with sound." By recording only on channel 1, rewinding the tape, and playing back channel 1 while recording on channel 2, duets could be played and recorded by one person.[9] Many commercial studios recorded a musical background on one tape channel and a vocalist on the other. This arrangement allowed musicians to play their parts and not be present while the vocalist's voice was recorded. The vocalist was then free to "experiment" as many times as necessary before deciding to keep a particular version of the song. This was the virtual beginning of "multi-tracking," a process that is to this day, invaluable.

Another feature found on many stereophonic reel-to-reel tape machines, was an effect known as "sound-on-sound." This was an extension of the "sound-with-sound" technique. Material was recorded on channel 1 and the tape re-wound. As new material was added by recording on channel 2, the playback signal from channel 1 could be mixed with it. When the tape was re-wound, both the material from channel 1, and what was previously on 2 was then mixed on channel 2, thus leaving channel 1 free again to add a third part. This process was limited by the noise added to each generation of recording. The more times a sound was "dubbed" (re-recorded), the weaker the primary signal with relation to the noise. Good stereophonic tape machines allowed two or three dubbings (generations of recording) of the signal with a somewhat adequate signal-to-noise ratio.

---

[9] *In fact, the guitarist Les Paul invented this technique. It was first used on the recording "Vaya con Dios" by his wife, Mary Ford, who was able, for the first time, to sing a duet with herself. For the 1950s, this was an incredible breakthrough in tape recording technology.*

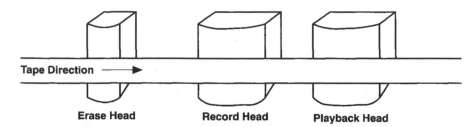

Figure 10-8. Arrangement of tape heads on a tape machine having separate record and playback heads.

On tape machines that used separate heads for recording and playback; the tape passes the record head before it passes the playback head. Using this arrangement, an "echo" effect could be produced electronically. Because there is a distance between the record and playback heads, a signal being recorded at the record head could be played back as the tape passed the playback head. The signal was delayed by the distance separating the two heads and the speed of the tape. If the signal being played back was then re-introduced into the record head, an "echo effect" was the result.

Other effects were possible. Construction of loops of pre-recorded tape made ostinato or repeated patterns. Two tape recorders could be used to combine features of each in the preparation of a recorded tape. Possibilities seemed endless for the recording, editing and composing of taped music. All that took place just before the age of digital music.

Audio for Film

The desire to add audio to video dates back to the late 19th century, when watching "moving pictures" became a highly popular form of entertainment. Around 1895, Thomas Edison mechanically coupled a phonograph player to a kinetoscope in an attempt to add audio to his work. Edison and others experimented with similar systems throughout the next decade, but achieving consistent synchronization (coupling) was problematic. Film was brittle and delicate, and breaks occurred often. Splicing the film placed the music out of sync with the action; much to the audience's dissatisfaction.

By the late 1920s, a new system for synchronizing sound and action on film was captivating audiences. This system placed the audio track linearly, directly on the film. Any timing modification to the film resulted in a corresponding modification to the audio track. Synchronization was maintained, and audiences were thrilled, although when frames of film were removed, subsequent "drop-outs" in the audio concomitantly occurred.

A similar system is still in place today. An optical analog of the desired audio track is recorded linearly on the side of the film. Light shining through the audio track is read by a photosensitive transducer, and is converted to electrical energy. This electrical signal is then amplified, and synchronized sound and video result.

DISCUSSION QUESTIONS FOR CHAPTER TEN

1.   Describe how sounds can be recorded without the aid of electrical circuitry.

2.   What are some of the advantages that electronic recording of sounds offer over the mechanical process?

3.   Discuss the various kinds of magnetic recording media that were available. Include thickness, length, width, packaging and coating in your discussion.

4.   Describe tape noise. How was it reduced in the recording process?

5.   What is the difference between "sound-with-sound" and "sound-on-sound" tape recording?

6.   Discuss "synchronization" as it relates to pairing recording devices; and as it relates to video with audio.

Digital Storage of Music

CHAPTER 11

Digital technology related to audio has followed closely the developments of the technology that fostered the age of computers. The storage and reproduction of analog acoustic events as binary digits is the subject of this chapter. The efficiency of binary codes to describe analog events enables digital circuitry to store and reproduce enormous amounts of data. First, look at the language that today's music machines use.

BINARY NUMBERS

The numbers that we use in daily life are "base 10" numbers. Ten different digits are used in different combinations to describe things numerically. Those digits are, 0, 1, 2, 3, 4, 5, 6, 7, 8, & 9. In the binary system (base 2), only two of these digits are used. In machine language, that means voltage on/off, or supplied/not supplied, with 1 being the "on" condition and 0, of course, being the "off" condition. As can be seen in Figure 11-1, binary **words**, or strings of 1s and 0s are needed to express meaning.

Decimal Base 10	Binary Base 2
0	0000
1	0001
2	0010
3	0011
4	0100
5	0101
6	0110
7	0111
8	1000
9	1001

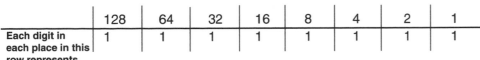

	128	64	32	16	8	4	2	1
Each digit in each place in this row represents the number above it.	1	1	1	1	1	1	1	1

> **WORD: A string of bits that together contain binary information.**

Figure 11-1.

143

There is an additional feature of binary notation that makes it suited for the encoding and processing of information. In base 2, from the right, each next place in the word represents a doubling of value. The right column represents 1's, the next column represents 2s, next is 4s, 8s, 16s, and so on. Therefore, in base 2, the code one, zero (or 0010 or 00010) would represent the digit "2" in base 10. Using this logic and Figure 11-1, take time now to double 2 (base 10, of course) and see how that number is represented in binary code. Now double that. How is it represented? In the figure below, 0111 represents the number 7. Here's how that works:

Row 1		128	64	32	16	8	4	2	1
Row 2	Each digit in each place in the top row represents the number above it.	0	0	0	0	0	1	1	1
Row 1 x Row 2		0	0	0	0	0	4 +	2 +	1 = 7

Figure 11-2.

Machines can make sense of and process this kind of information much faster than extracting meaning from ten different kinds of digits. It is this simplicity and its speed that makes the digital domain so usable for information processing.[1] These base 2 codes are called BInary digiTs, or, as we know them, **BIT**s.

Using Boolean logic and combinations of bits, a number of simple commands called **operators** have been formed to design and create logic circuits. These commands do a great deal of the electronic processing that goes on in our digital electronic components. Even quite simple commands can, in combination, cause complex operations to occur. The logic goes something like this: "If this set of circumstances occurs, then do this." In other words, when a particular number is generated (from 0 to 255 in an 8 bit system), a pre-determined set of instructions (operators) is called into action by the computer. By using simple combinations of operators, and even combining these with other single or combinations of operators, more complex commands can be created. Tremendous quantities of data can be directed, catalogued, tested, and processed; all, at nearly the speed of light. The development of the microchip (solid state circuitry) has made digital signal processing feasible. Instead of rooms full of vacuum tubes performing logical functions by turning circuits on and off, these same processes can be completed using circuits printed on small boards using

BIT: A binary digit. Bits are either 1 or 0; i.e., on or off, voltage or no voltage conditions.

OPERATOR: Logic algorithms in Boolean algebra. Combination commands that route digital signals to control complex operations.

---

[1] *The binary system is based upon Boolean algebra. This algebraic system was first described in 1854 by George Boole in a work titled* An Investigation of the Laws of Thought, On Which Are Founded the Mathematical Theories of Logic and Probabilities.

microchips as part of their design. Combinations of boards, each dedicated to its own function, give us the methodology to create a whole new generation of electronic devices; not the least of which is digital audio circuitry.

ANALOG VERSUS DIGITAL

We know that audio events, such as music, can be encoded on recording tape in the form of continuous magnetic voltage fluctuations. The analog system must strive to complete a continuous audio picture of the original sound. In contrast, a digital recording of these events converts audio information into thousands of "still" pictures per second of the waveforms as they enter the recording device. Just as our visual sense converts twenty-four frames per second of a succession of individual still pictures into what we see as continuous motion in movies, our audio sense makes similar conversions with sound. The digital system not only takes pictures (samples) of the signals, it also checks these samples to make sure that each makes sense with reference to its position within the waveform. There is continuous correction of the signal as it is recorded and played back. Pohlmann compares analog and digital audio phenomena using the analogy of two full buckets.[2] If one bucket is full of water (an analog analogy) and the other, full of ball bearings (digits, of course), and we want to know how much is contained in each bucket; then to determine the volume of material, different procedures would be used. We could dip the water from the pail into a calibrated measuring container, thus determining the volume of its contents. By doing so, some water might be spilled and some evaporation will certainly take place. While we can get a fair approximation of the volume, we will never get an exact measurement. The bucket of ball bearings in the other pail might have its contents counted as one way to describe the volume of material. And even if we did transfer them to the measuring container, the contents would not be lost if we were careful. As can be seen, it is an easier process to keep track of and more precisely describe the contents of the bucket containing the ball bearings. In a quite similar fashion, at first it might seem that analog recording might be more faithful to the original, yet it turns out that in fact, digits do the job more precisely.[3]

To record and reproduce music using an analog system, we need a microphone, preamplifier, master tape recorder, (or master record cutter), and playback system that is also comprised of a number of components, such as pre-amplifiers, filters (EQ) and speakers. Each step in this process has inherent difficulties concerning the introduction of analog distortion and noise into the

---

[2] *Pohlmann, Ken C.,* Principles of Digital Audio, *second edition, (Carmel, IN: SAMS, A division of Prentice-Hall Computer Publishing), 1992, pp. 38 - 40.*

[3] *Let the record show that the author did not say "better." While digital processing of an audio signal may be more precise, the final product will sound "different" than an analog counterpart. While both final products can be judged as pleasing, personal preference, learning, past experience, prejudice and personal judgement will be the final determining factors as to what is chosen as "better."*

signal. The digital process, on the other hand, takes the analog signal, converts it into a stream of binary information that is processed as numeric information, then stores it as a magnetic imprint. Sometimes this imprint is stored on compact discs, and more recently on **flash drives** but the point is that the process is reversed only at playback, by the consumer. Using digits, the chain of events is simpler and there is less chance for distortion and noise to be introduced into the playback. Now, let's look at why this is so.

ANALOG TO DIGITAL CONVERSION
Sampling

As was learned earlier, the parameter of human hearing is approximately from 20Hz to 20,000Hz (20kHz), and from approximately -20 dB to 110 dB SPL. It is these frequencies and amplitudes then that are the parameters of concern in the audio digital domain. Compact Disc (CD) quality audio **sampling** is accomplished at the rate of 44,100 times per second and the information is converted to digital code in the form of binary bits.[4]

It might seem to some that even at this rate, there are discrete "holes" in the information, i.e., areas between these 44,100 samples, each second, where information is not present. In actuality, when the stored samples are sent on to the **digital to analog (D/A) converter**,[5] the entire analog waveform signal is recreated. But more about that later. Of more concern here, is why and how this sampling rate was chosen. Sounds of extremely low frequency can be easily sampled because of their relatively long wavelengths. Obviously, many samples are taken of each period of vibration in a 20 Hz tone. However, at 20,000Hz, it can be readily seen that only about two samples per wavelength can be taken (44,100 samples per second / 20,000Hz = 2.205Hz). Let's explore what happens and why enough samples are present for a complete reconstruction of the signal.

Sampling theory states that the sampling rate must be double the highest audio frequency.[6] Because our human hearing mechanisms do not respond to audio stimuli higher that 20kHz, all higher frequencies are filtered out of the incoming signal using a **low pass filter** (in this case, anything above 20kHz). Let's assume that we are sampling audio that contains complex waveforms in this threshold range (for instance the harmonic content of an E^b clarinet's high register). As the clarinet sound is sampled, harmonics produced by the instrument above the 20,000Hz level are eliminated by filters. This "simplifying" of the harmonic structure leaves us with a less complex wave form. It is not a con-

FLASH DRIVE: A digital storage medium that connects to a computerized device via a serial interface (USB-Universal Serial Bus) "Flash Drive" is a misnomer, in that it uses no moving parts. Also known as Jump Drive, USB Drive, Thumb Drive (because of its small size) Flash Rom, or Flash Ram.

SAMPLING: The process by which the entire analog audible frequency spectrum is assessed or scanned 44,100 times per second and the information (the entire audio spectrum) converted to binary code.

DIGITAL TO ANALOG CONVERTER: D/A converters transduce binary code into voltage fluctuations. Conversely, A/D converters transduce voltage variances to binary coded signals.

LOW PASS FILTER: An electronic device that allows only frequencies lower than a given cutoff point to pass. In the digital domain, any frequencies below 20 kHz.

---

[4] *Manufacturers have agreed upon this sampling rate for the compact disc so that all audio equipment can be compatible.*

[5] *Both Analog to Digital and Digital to Analog converters are referred to by their initials: D/A converters and A/D converters.*

[6] Shannon,C.E., "*A Mathematical Theory of Communication,*" Bell System Technical Journal # 27, 1948.

146

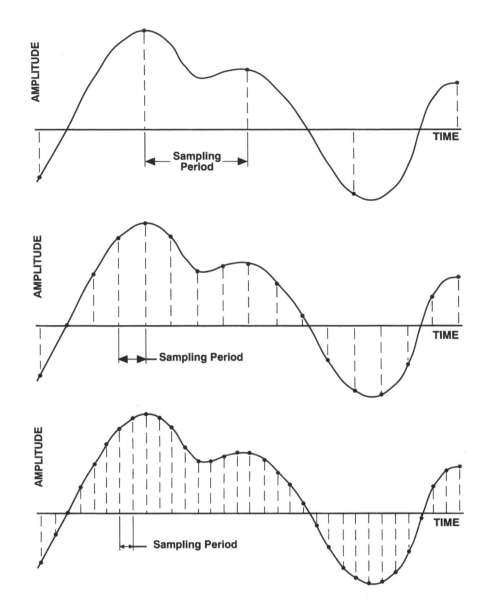

Figure 11-3. Discrete time sampling divides a signal into equal, periodically spaced intervals. The higher the sampling rate, the smaller the sampling period.

cern to us however, because we could never have heard those harmonics anyway. The two samples of this 20kHz tone per waveform (not per second) are enough to reconstruct the harmonics as simple sine waves. In other words, doubling the sampling rate of the highest frequency that can be heard gives a picture of all the information that human hearing can use, and discards the rest. CD quality audio utilizes 16 bit **bytes** (words), and records 44,100 of them per second. This results in sound with a high frequency cutoff of 22,050 Hz. Higher sampling rates are available.

DVD quality audio supports up to 24 bit bytes, records audio at 192,000 samples per second, and has a high frequency cutoff of 96,000 Hz. Although we

BYTE: An 8 bit binary word.

147

can't hear harmonics much above 20,000 Hz, audiophiles claim that preserving those higher harmonics allows them to sum with the lower harmonic components of each musical tone, creating more realistic music, representative of what humans really hear when listening to acoustic musical instruments.

In actuality, CD or DVD quality audio sampling occurs not only at the stated sample rates of 44.1kHz and 192kHz per second, but at rates much higher. This **oversampling** is created in order to improve error correction and reduce the effects of problems (called ALIASING) that may be caused when very high frequencies are removed from sampled audio signals.

Quantization

When an audio signal is recorded, two dimensions of information are required; frequency and amplitude. While the sampling process catalogs frequency information, **quantization** saves amplitude information. As each sample is taken, the voltage level (the electronic equivalent of amplitude) is also sampled and this value is saved in binary code. The accuracy of this value is limited by the ability of the A/D converter to store this information. Resolution is the issue. If, for instance, a sample's signal strength is 1.374 volts, and our A/D converter can only save data as 1.0 volts or 1.5 volts, the final signal would suffer from less than perfect resolution. It would be rounded up and the value saved as 1.5 volts. In the binary system, word length is the determining factor as to how many quantizing intervals are available. The more bits available, the less the error, and the greater the resultant signal resolution. Logically, it can be seen that there will always be some measurement error. In fact, this parameter can never be perfect due to systemic limitations.[7] Almost all manufacturers have agreed that 16 to 24 bit words are long enough so that amplitude errors are audibly indistinguishable. It is this feature that has made the CD format so attractive. Longer words would however, provide more signal resolution. A 16 bit word provides 65,536 intervals. That's 2 multiplied by itself 16 times. The longer the binary word, the greater the amplitude resolution.

Format

Data are stored in binary code, in the form of **frames**. These frames contain not only the recorded, digitized signal (8 bits per stereo channel of CD quality audio) but also synchronization codes, identification, address information and even redundancy data for error correction at playback. Actually, each frame contains many data words, and the way this information is stored determines the **format** for the system. Different storage systems store data in different formats. There is considerable latitude involved in the determination of frame format.

OVERSAMPLING: In some CD players, samples of no voltage are created between actual samples so comparisons can be made among all samples, and a complete and accurate set of digits is the result, even if the original signal has been lost or degraded in some manner. This happens at either 4, 8 or 16 times per frame.

QUANTIZATION: The representation of a complete voltage span (level or intensity) in discrete, binary numbers. It is the digital representation of amplitude level.

FRAME: The smallest recognizable complete sample of data.

FORMAT: The arrangement of bits, words and codes within a frame. Many formats are possible, and each electronic component in the digital domain reads only those frames that are formatted for that system.

---

[7] *If your ruler measures only in increments of ¹⁄₁₆th of an inch, that's the closest you can get to accurate measurement. If it has increments of ¹⁄₃₂nd, or ¹⁄₆₄th of an inch, finer and finer measurements can be made. So it is with bits of audio information. The more bits available, the more accurate is the quantization.*

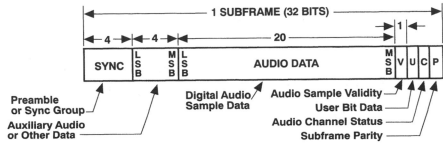

Figure 11-4. The AES/EBU serial interface uses a subframe of 32 bits.

Digital audio recording begins as a serial process. That is, data are transduced as a stream of bits. It is encoded and recorded as frames in parallel, i.e., with the bits for each frame recorded next to each other.[8] Although frames are stored in parallel (side-by-side), when they are to be played back, they are again read in series, as a bit stream going into the D/A converter.[9] The format defines the whereabouts of a number of terms in an audio sample. An audio sample is a signal that has been sampled periodically, quantized, represented in binary code as an 8 bit word and matched with its 8 bit word stereo counterpart. A subframe is audio data from one stereo channel coupled with other auxiliary information regarding time codes and redundant checking information. Two subframes make up a frame. The rate of transmissions of frames is the same as the sampling rate. Besides the two channels of audio information, each frame contains eight bits of information coded to regulate starting, stopping, time between selections, time information, and all TOC (table of contents) information. Information stored in this configuration, today, is called "stereo interleaved," and is a standard component of the CD quality audio format.

Data are stored as 32 bit words. While each frame contains 32 bits, two **bytes** are stored as audio signal information. Figure 11-4 shows the format used in the AES/EBU system used by most consumer digital audio devices.[10] In the S/PDIF-2 format (Sony/Phillips Digital Interface Format) developed by the Sony Corporation for professional audio use, bits 1–20 are reserved for audio information. Bits 21–25 are there for future expansion, and bits 26–32 hold information that orients and controls the process.

---

[8] *Think of this process as the bits being members of a marching band. They enter in single file and are lined up and stored in ranks of 8, 16, or 20. They are grouped in their ranks (words, frames and codes) according to what they represent. When they leave, they do so in single file.*

[9] *There is much more to the coding and interfacing of digital frames and subframes. The reader is directed to the following excellent source for further information:*
Pohlmann, K. C. Principles of Digital Audio, second edition, (Carmel, IN: SAMS, A division of Prentice-Hall Computer Publishing), 1992, 474 pgs.
This chapter is based, in large measure, on this excellent chronicle of the digital audio domain.

[10] *Refers to Audio Engineering Society (AES), European Broadcast Union (EBU). A format based on this system has been endorsed by the International Electrotechnical Commission (IEC) for consumer digital audio equipment.*

DIGITAL SIGNAL STORAGE

Pulse Code Modulation

Although there are many ways to encode digital or binary information, **pulse code modulation (PCM)** is the system the audio industry has chosen to store audio information. It seems to be the most effective form of binary representation for this application.

We have seen how audio data is converted to binary information and coded as a series of bits, words, subframes and frames that represent samples and quantized data from the analog signal by the analog to digital converter. In order to store this information, binary numbers are sent to the recording device as a series of pulses that represent the signal's amplitude. If the signal is stereo, this pulse code data is **multiplexed** to form one data stream.[11] Since binary coding is used, the system easily keeps track of signal processing and error detection information. When it comes time for playback, the PCM signal is simply decoded using a D/A converter to reconstruct the original waveform information.

Digital Magnetic Recording

The storage of analog signals on magnetic tape was the backbone of the recording industry for the last half of the twentieth century. Its unique abilities to store and reproduce, cut and paste, and erase and reuse have made it indispensable. Its drawbacks have been covered in the last chapter. Tape then became the primary candidate for the storage of digital information as well. The large amount of data generated by digital systems to be stored, put unique demands on even the most sophisticated recorder.

Although today's digital recordings take advantage of the ever-increasing availability of computer storage capacity, earlier digital recordings were stored on magnetic recording tape. An analog tape recorder must be responsive to about 20 kHz or the limit of human hearing. Digital systems require that a sampling rate of 44.1 kHz be accommodated because, although information comes in as a stream of bits, it must be multiplied by 16 (the minimum number of bits per frame), or over 700 kilobits per second. If room is added for information concerning synchronization and error correction, as much as 1000 kHz (1 mHz) could be needed. In actuality, with pulse code modulation, only about 1/2 of

---

PULSE CODE MODULATION: PCM is any kind of digital encoding of a signal. The most common type is where the voltage range is divided into a number of equal intervals. This quantization is called "Linear PCM."

MULTIPLEX: When two or more signals are combined in such a way that they can later be decoded or separated they are said to be "multiplexed."

[11] *Stereo multiplexing is also accomplished in many FM broadcasts. In this technique, the left and right signal channels are added together to form a "sum" signal, and are also subtracted to form a "difference" signal. The sum signal is what is decoded by a monaural radio. The difference signal is used to control a 38kHz "subcarrier," which is not detected by a monaural receiver. This processed subcarrier is then mixed with the sum signal so that it, too, controls the subcarrier. Thus the carrier signal is actually controlled by both the sum and difference signals. To recover the original stereo signal, the sum and difference signals are decoded. The process, for you mathematicians, is as follows: $(L+R) + (L-R) = 2L$ and $(L+R) - (L-R) = 2R$. The entire process is used just so that monaural receivers can also pick up the full signal. Before FM multiplexing, radio stations sometimes broadcast the left channel on FM and the right channel on AM. Listeners with two radios could get an early form of stereo sensation in this way.*

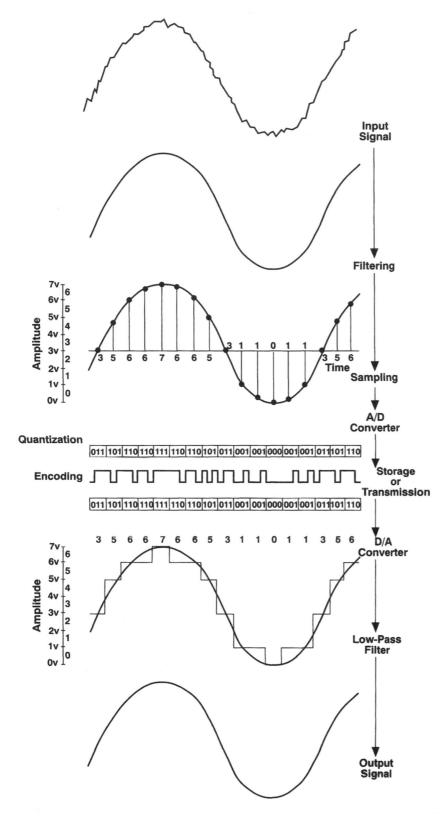

Figure 11-5. Graphical representation of the signal flow in a complete PCM digitization system.

151

that rate is necessary. Still, the bandwidth of a digital signal is about 25 times larger than its analog counterpart. If this begins to look like an insurmountable problem, rest assured that it is not. An analog audio signal must be stored linearly as a composite signal in real time. A digitized signal need not be stored in this fashion. It is possible, for instance, to increase the density of the digital signal many times (the amount of information stored at any given location on the recording tape), because a somewhat distorted waveform of digits can be decoded without including this distortion. With as much as a million bits of information per second, per channel conceivably coming into a digital recorder at any one time, this seems a really complex process. This is the beauty of the processing power of the binary system.

COMPACT DISC TECHNOLOGY

While at first glance, the compact disc might be likened to today's version of the LP record, the likeness is actually rather limited. A compact disc's information is stored under the surface of the disc. Its information is a series of pits imbedded in the disc's substrata, and the information is read by a **laser**[12] light from the center of the disc, out. There are other differences as well.

The compact disc is a rather amazing invention. It stores about 5 billion bits of audio information on a disc that is slightly smaller than 4 3/4 inches in diameter.[13] Information is stored as two 16 bit words sampled at 44.1 kHz. In 1974, the Phillips Corporation began looking at the possibilities of optical storage of audio and video signals. At about the same time, Sony was studying error correction methods in the digital domain. During this period in audio history, other electronics companies were also experimenting with the concept of an optically read digital audio disc. In 1979, an agreement was reached between the Sony Corporation and Phillips as to the audio format and the kind and size of disc to be used, and in 1982, Japan and Europe saw the very first CDs.[14] This unique, new, digital storage medium came to the United States marketplace in 1983, and although there is a long and detailed story concerning the development of the laser pickup, digital to analog conversion and other circuitry, the point is that the CD has possibly become the most successful electronic device ever introduced into the consumer marketplace.

LASER: In a CD "read" device, a special Light Emitting Diode (LED). This single wavelength light beam is filtered and focused on a very discrete area of the track so that it can read the pits that are there.

[12] *LASER is an acronym for "light amplification from stimulated emission of radiation."*

[13] *Legend has it that the Phillips Corporation of the Netherlands contacted the (then) conductor of the Berlin Philharmonic Orchestra, Herbert von Karajan, to determine how much audio information should be able to be stored on one compact disc. His advice was that a CD should hold the complete Beethoven Ninth Symphony without interruption, or about 74 minutes of music. Indeed, and behold, the CD holds 74 minutes, 33 seconds of information. It seems curious that Ludwig van Beethoven may have determined the length of our most popular electronic storage medium in the year 1823.*

[14] *"The Digital Audio Disc Committee," a group representing more than thirty-five audio manufacturers, adopted the "Compact Disc Digital Audio System," as a collaborative effort. This ten-year development of the CD stands in stark contrast to the almost single-handed efforts of Thomas Edison while inventing the wax cylinder phonograph.*

The Disc

The compact disc (in the format properly called CD-Audio) is encoded on only one side. Although double-sided discs are possible (DVD discs can be encoded on both sides), it is cheaper to manufacture two one-sided discs than one that is double sided. The side not encoded is imprinted with the label. The disc has a transparent protective layer forming the surface. Under that is a reflective layer to allow the laser beam to "read" the reflected signals. These are in the form of pits in the metalized surface. The *edge* of each pit (both front edge and back edge) is read as a "one" in binary code, with the areas between pits being read as zeros. The length of the pits and the surface between pits vary according to the content of the signal, with the reading of between 4 and 11 zeros being possible there. The surface of the disc is time sampled and frequency data are thus decoded. This PCM (pulse code modulation) actually contains more data than one might think. By reading the edges of the pits as 1s and the areas, both in the pits and between them as 0s, four pits can actually reconstruct 31 bits of information.

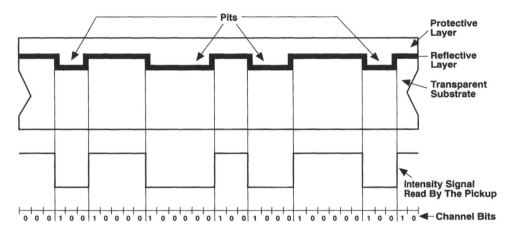

Figure 11-7. Transitions between pit bottom and disc surface, or "land," represent binary 1s; flats represent binary 0s.

As we have seen, data are encoded by the A/D converter into 32 bit frames. A frame is the smallest recognizable complete sample of data that can be stored. It contains both the binary words and binary decoding information. Data are encoded on CDs so that six audio sampling periods (both left and right channels) are stored as one frame. By doing so, decoding information from each sample can be compared. In actuality, during the reconstruction of the audio waveform in the D/A converter, bits from other frames are also compared and error free waveforms become the analog result. One hundred and thirty-six frames of binary audio information constitute one second of real time audio. The process requires that data be digitally packaged in unique form before being stored on the CD; and the CD player is required to decode discs into the original electronic voltage fluctuations sensed first by the microphone.

153

CDs are manufactured with one of three possible kinds of audio history: DDD, ADD or AAD. This legend can be found somewhere on almost all CD labels. The first letter refers to the way the music was recorded (digital or analog). The middle letter concerns the mastering of the tape, and the last tells us that the signal on our CD is stored digitally.

The mastering of compact discs is accomplished in a "clean room" using an extremely fine grade of glass. The glass master has its pits exposed by a computer-operated laser cutter, and then the glass is washed in a developing fluid where the exposed pits are etched away. Engraving is stopped when the glass is etched to the depth of the substrata. Following development, an extremely fine coating of (usually) silver is evaporated onto the surface of the glass. In a separate process, a nickel coating is electroplated to the glass disc. This metal plate is then separated from the glass, forming what is known as the "father." Using the same electroplating process, a number of positive impressions; "mother discs" are created; and from these, the process continues making "sons," or negative submasters. It is from these that CDs are manufactured. After many procedures were tried, the usual process for creating CDs is to have molten polycarbonate material injected into a vacuum form mold. The center hole is formed in the same process. After cooling, a layer of aluminum, silver or gold is evaporated onto the disc for reflectivity. The metal layer is then covered with an acrylic layer for protecting the surface from scratches, abrasions and oxidation. Following inspection, packaging and wrapping, discs are ready for distribution.

Today's personal computers are capable of recording data to discs playable in CD and DVD players. This is accomplished by using a laser to "burn" digital patterns into a special media located under the clear polycarbonate surface of the disc. Re-writeable CD and DVD discs use a recording media that when heated by the laser, returns to its original state, prior to being rewritten.

The CD Player

The CD player serves the same purpose that the turntable does in analog reproduction. It makes the disc go round and it houses the optical pickup that actually reads the disc's information. The turning or rotating of the CD is accomplished quite differently from the way a turntable has to do its turning of a record. Turntables are asked to rotate faithfully at a constant speed of 33-1/3 rotations per minute. The CD player must read pits that were recorded at a constant linear velocity (CLV) on a spiral track. That means that the laser reader moves from near the center of the disc at its start, to the outer edge, and it must rotate the disc from about eight revolutions per second at the start, to approximately 3.5 rps at the outer edge. That's from 480 rpm down to about 210 rpm, as the spiral track's diameter gets ever larger. The CD player is responsible for adjusting its speed as the disc turns.

The optical pickup consists of the lens structure, the laser source, and the reader. Its housing is constructed so that it moves smoothly across the disc's radius. It moves in response to the tracking information that it reads from the disc.

It is also responsive to user controlled random access programming. Sensing the information encoded as pits on the CD is the job of laser light. Three beams of laser light are used to make sure that the middle beam reads the proper track. One beam reads ahead, one tracks the middle, and one beam trails the other two. While no difference in sound quality can be heard, older, one beam systems do not have the error detection and correction capability that three beam configurations have. It is this three beam system that allows oversampling to occur. Larger "chunks" of data are read at one time, compared and averaged. Then, corrections are made in the bit stream that concur with data from the majority of the frames that have been oversampled.

These three laser light beams are reflected by a lens at 90 degrees to their source and focused on the substrata of the CD containing the pits. When the light hits an area between pits, almost all of the light is reflected back. When the light encounters a pit, less than half of that intensity is read. The higher intensity reflections are read as zeros and the lesser intensity onsets (the edges of the pits) are read as ones. Some of the digital signals read by the laser light are used to keep the motion and focusing aspects of the motor doing its job properly.[15] The three beam system of tracking does a remarkable job of not only keeping the focused center laser beam in the proper track, it also serves to put it back in the proper place if a bump or jar occurs. This ability, of course, has its limits, but without any mechanical means of physically holding the optical scanning mechanism in place, CDs have remarkable tracking and recovery capabilities.

In essence, 1 bit sampling, often promoted by the manufacturers of consumer electronics, operates at a sample rate much higher than 44.1kHz when converting digital samples to analog audio. Rather than determining the value of each byte prior to processing, the value of each bit is determined and processed. This reduces the need to oversample for error correction. Because 1 bit processing relies on a current similar to bias current during the conversion process, some claim that audible noise is introduced into the audio signal.

A **servo** motor controls the optical scanning system. It is responsible for moving the laser from one CD track to another, and for fast forward and reverse scanning. Three beam pickups are mounted under the place where the CD sits, on a "sled" that moves across the radius of the disc. Less precise, one beam systems are mounted on a radial arm that swings across the radius of the disc in an arc.

Other CD Formats

Describing the existing technological variations on the "CD theme" was an ever evolving story. Formats come and formats go. Basically, the trend is that audio and video technologies are being married into "multimedia" formats, containing audio, video, MIDI, html code, and more. In other words, still pictures, book text, graphic images and motion pictures are being integrated into what

SERVO: Shortened form of "servo-mechanism." A control system device that uses feedback of an output signal to compare and correct itself to a reference signal.

---

[15] *The spiral track on a CD is so narrow that thirty of them spiraling toward the outer edge of the disc cover only the width of a human hair.*

was once audio playback. Limiting factors for this development are the different types of digital formats and the amount of digital memory available at a given instant. Many people in the field say that they have begun to see the outer limits of the satisfactory uses of optical discs and are therefore turning to computer hard drives, DVD-R and FLASH RAM as the storage systems capable of storing and playing back enough binary information to make full motion analog video (30 video frames per second) and "be-in-the-sound" audio.

By encoding signals in binary formats, it is possible to display them as visual representations as well as aural ones, if the proper electronic encoding and decoding is done. Decoded music then, can also be represented as notation or even as an oscilloscopic signal, at the flick of a finger. We are in the midst of an evolution of remarkable changes in audio and visual storage and the distribution of music, pictures and the printed word. Below are some of the audio/video formats that are now commercially available. Hang on, catch up, or be left behind!

MP3 Technology

Presently, the CD is approaching the end of its technological reign, as more and more consumers turn to **MP3** and similar technologies as a preferred format for storing audio. MP3 stands for "Moving Pictures Experts Group," Audio Layer 3, and is in actuality, a compression scheme for decreasing the size of digital audio packets while maintaining satisfactory fidelity. This technology takes advantage of not only developments in digital technology, but also findings in the field of perceptual psychology. MP3 compression is accomplished by compromising portions of the audio spectrum, deemed inaudible to humans. CD quality audio requires 10 megabytes of storage for every minute of stereo audio, and MP3 technology has reduced this by roughly a 10:1 ratio. The standard MP3 file, like CD audio, uses 16 bit bytes at a sample rate of 44,100 samples per second (stereo interleaved, of course). The quality of the MP3 file is determined by its bit rate; that is, the number of bits delivered per second. At its inception, 128 thousand bits per second (128kbps) were deemed satisfactory, but consumers soon began to notice diminished audio quality when compared to other digital formats. Now, rates of 160kbps and higher are standard.

While the computer hard drive remains a viable storage medium, Flash-ROM drives, having no moving parts, lower manufacturing and shipping costs, and a much smaller "footprint," are rapidly replacing them as the preferred device for music storage. As of this writing it is possible to purchase music stored on Flash-Rom "jump drives."

MP3: A compressed digital audio file, reduced in size according to psychoacoustical findings related to the limits of human audio perception. A generic term for any number of similar compression schemes including AAC (Advanced Audio Coding), Apple Lossless Compression, Ogg Vorbis, MP4 and whatever the future delivers.

Memory

It was not that long ago when computer users discussed computer memory in terms of kilobytes. As technology advanced, megabyte storage was at the forefront. We discuss memory, today, in terms of gigabytes, and terabyte storage is becoming an affordable reality. Petabyte storage capacity cannot be far away.

1024 bytes = 1 kilobyte
1024 kilobytes = 1 megabyte
1024 megabytes = 1 gigabyte
1024 gigabytes = 1 terabyte
1024 terabytes = 1 petabyte

Where Do We Go From Here?

Our technological conveniences are merging in the modern digital world. We once possessed telephones, record players, radios, tape players, cameras and television sets as separate contrivances. Today, our cell phones play MP3 files take photographs and display video. Our personal computers record and edit audio, video, and burn CDs and DVDs. What we once called "date books" are now personal digital assistants (PDAs), affording us the same conveniences as the former devices, and include "smart" calendars featuring programmed reminders, alarm clocks, and more. Even our books and magazines are available to us without paper, displayed instead on LCD monitors.

As of this writing we are beginning to move away from owning the bits and bytes that produce music, and instead will rent them in the form of streaming audio and video—digital music and video signals—beamed from satellites, high above earth, providing content to our cell phones and PDAs, that we've preselected via personal playlists. Today, the sky really is the limit.

DISCUSSION QUESTIONS FOR CHAPTER ELEVEN

1. Describe in your own words, the differences between analog and digital information.

2. Using only Figure 11-1, how would the number ten be represented in binary coding?

3. Trace the path of a sound as it enters a microphone and exits a speaker if it had been stored digitally.

4. Describe the relative advantages and disadvantages of DVD, Compact Discs and flash drives as archive media. Are there other, better formats?

5. Relate the "concept" of digital audio to its marriage with video. Do the same with its marriage to the computer.

6. Discuss the use of today's cell phones, PDAs, and MP3 players in relation to digital audio and future music listening habits of the human species.

Electronic Production of Sounds

CHAPTER 12

ELECTRONIC AMPLIFICATION OF TRADITIONAL INSTRUMENTS

Throughout the 1950s, a new popular music sensation was beginning—subsequently, it became known as rock music. While it was not called "rock" at first, or even "rock 'n roll," followers of this new music that covered "hillbilly," "blues" and "rhythm and blues" traditions massed in large audiences. It was even quite fashionable for young listeners to scream during performances. The fact that the "older" generation (and "musicians") did not like the new style only served to make it more popular with America's adolescent population.[1] Unlike the big bands of the nineteen thirty's and forty's that had enough instruments to be heard over noisy, energetic audiences, these rock musicians played in groups of only four or five musicians, and they played on acoustic instruments. Often, it became difficult to hear them during live concerts. More sophisticated electronic amplification was developed because it offered solutions to this really important and immediate problem. This exploration to make acoustic music louder ultimately caused music to change in a number of ways, and the music industry would never again be the same. This chapter covers some of the changes in contemporary music's sound and the instruments that have been developed, due largely to this phenomenon.[2]

It would serve us well to have the changes to American popular music put into some historical perspective. In 1970, Paul Ackerman, then editor of *Billboard* magazine put it this way:

> Rhythm and Blues, the popular music of the black man, spawned the "Rock" era. The period of gestation was the 1940's, a decade that saw the development of profound changes both in the music industry and the nation itself.
>
> During this decade, the band business was to finally enter a decline (editor's note: "Bands" here, refer to the large dance orchestras of the 1930s and 1940s.). Public tastes were changing and so were the economics of the mu-

---

[1] *Elvis.*

[2] *Serious electronic music was already being experimented with before 1955, the time when America's popular music began to change. Milton Babbit, for instance, was composing with and developing the RCA **synthesizer** in New York City (it took up an entire city block). Major funding for experimentation with new music technology, however, happened mostly in the area of music that produced revenue!*

sic industry. Bands became increasingly unprofitable. This created a vacuum that would soon make possible the emergence into the mass pop market, an exciting music hitherto known as one of the 'specialty fields.' Facilitating the entry into the pop field of this basic American idiom, Rhythm and Blues, was the improvement in communications. Radio, television and the growth of the airlines inaugurated a new day in cosmopolitanism. The boundaries, or lines of demarcation separating cultural groups tended to become indistinct, with the result that the general population became exposed to the musical cultures of heretofore isolated people ...and the broad pop market liked what it heard. The Rhythm and Blues artists brought to musical America a style of performance and a body of song material that was fresh, honest, and the very antithesis of the traditional 'Tin Pan Alley' type of material.

This crucial development in pop music reached a peak in the 1950s, at which time, white pop artists realizing the power of R&B material, covered R&B hits. The trend became known as 'Rock and Roll,' a phrase rooted in blues terminology and popularized by the late disc jockey, Alan Freed, and others.

Thus did Rock and Roll bring something new and valid to the music business and to the American society: a merging of musical categories that prepared the way for Elvis Presley and (later) the Beatles.

Today Rock and Roll is a term little used. The modern version is 'Rock,' of which there are many forms. But the mother of it all is 'Rhythm and Blues.'[3]

Since the development of the public address system in the 1920s, singers and instrumentalists have used microphones to amplify their music. Electric guitars were introduced in the 1930s that featured electronic "pickups" developed to transduce vibrations directly from instrument bodies and strings. These pick-ups are not actually microphones since they are not very sensitive to sounds propagated through air, but rather, they detect and amplify vibration directly from the bodies or strings of instruments. As a result, guitars and acoustic string basses no longer needed the acoustic body that acted as an amplifier. Soon, electric basses, in smaller sizes, began to be manufactured for use with a shoulder strap, and they were worn across the shoulders like a guitar. These instruments began to be manufactured from solid wooden boards and later, from fiberglass and other man-made materials. Because those early electronic guitars didn't sound exactly like their acoustic counterparts, a new instrumental sound was created. Rock followers liked the new "electronic" sound. They even learned to appreciate those "squeaks" and "squeals" that we acousticians identify as "feedback."[4]

---

[3] Rock Begins, Volume I , *excerpted liner notes by Paul Ackerman; (New York: ATCO Records,1970, record no. SD 33-314).*

[4] *The re-introduction of an instrument's sound into an acoustically coupled system allows it to be re-amplified. As this sound loop happens, the frequency quickly rises. It continues through the frequency spectrum. Each pass through the amplifier makes it louder. Rock musicians soon discovered that the frequency and amplitude of feedback could be manipulated by the instrument's proximity to the speaker.*

Even the distorted, fuzzy over-amplification of the instrument's sounds came to be used and enjoyed by musicians and audiences alike.[5]

As the popularity of amplified guitars and basses grew, musicians and electrical engineers, excited by the possibilities of amplifying those sounds, developed a variety of pickups featuring different characteristics and frequency responses. Violin and bass pickups were fashioned, and even specialty microphones that reject ambient noise while capturing frequencies specific to certain instruments were developed as well. These are available today for almost any acoustic instrument.

Early Electronic Pianos

In the late 1940s, transducers were developed to electronically amplify the strings of a piano.[6] Normally, if a piano's sounding board is removed, the strings produce only a weak sound. But when a small transducer (Figure 12-1) was placed near the string, its sound could be electronically amplified many times. This method of amplification employed a magnet within a coil of wire.

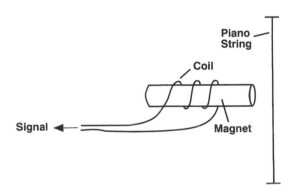

Figure 12-1. A simplified cross-section of a magnetic transducer for a piano string.

As the position of the metal string varies as it vibrates in relation to the magnet, electrical changes are generated in the magnetic field, sensed by the coil, and sent as voltage fluctuations to an amplifier. Another form of electronic pickup (Figure 12-2) utilized the string as one member of the electrical circuit. In this case, as the position of the string and the metal plate vary in relation to each other, voltage changes were created and sent on to an amplifier.

---

[5] *"Sex, Drugs & Rock 'n' Roll" gave America's youth its culture and values in the mid-to-late '60s. A search for "relevance" was undertaken. Rock music responded with feedback, reverb, fuzz tone, tone bends, and other interesting noise-makers to accompany the "mind tripping." The stranger the music, the more the youth seemed to like it. Flower children, hippies and groupies became a part of the American scene, as the "establishment" became more and more nervous about what was happening to music and to youth. Youth, on the other hand, did not like what was happening to the world, and openly talked about it in their music.*
Wagner, Erik, Excerpted from an unpublished paper, Miami-Dade Community College, 1993.

[6] *Olsen, Harry F., Musical Engineering, (New York: McGraw-Hill Book Company, 1952), p. 127.*

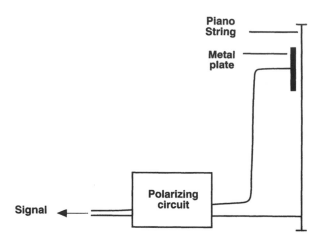

Figure 12-2. A simplified cross-section of an electrical transducer for a piano string.

As would be expected, the positioning of the transducer along the lengths of the strings was critical. If it was placed opposite a node, where little or no vibration was taking place, no voltage could be sensed. Electronic pianos utilizing this kind of transducer were popular for a time, but are no longer being manufactured. Later, electronic pianos made use of metal bars as sound sources that were struck by a conventional piano mechanism. The vibrations of the metal bars were transduced and their signals amplified. They were played back through speakers mounted in the rear of the piano cabinet, or through headphones. The sound envelope of this kind of electronic piano had an initial attack and sustain portion somewhat similar to a conventional piano. However, the decay and the relative strengths of the metal bar's harmonic series had sonically different characteristics compared to the acoustic piano.

Some manufacturers took advantage of the fact that sounds produced by electronic means were not quite the same as the sounds of a conventional piano. Many added electronic devices that further altered the tone. An electronic vibrato device (frequency modulation) and a tremolo mechanism (amplitude modulation) were developed and added to some models. Others offered electronic reverberation (described later in this chapter), and some early electronic pianos had a control that made an unusually long "sustain" possible.

Electronic Pickups

The guitar, since it became an electronically amplified instrument, has gained widespread popularity, especially in popular music.[7] The pickup is

---

[7] *The electric guitar was invented by guitarist Les Paul. He took the amplifier from an AM radio, attached a pick-up to his guitar, and attached it to a speaker. By adding a microphone pick-up, he began a pop music tradition.*

located at the bridge of the instrument, and the hollow, conventional acoustic body is often times replaced by a solid body that can be quite thin, since no acoustic resonator is needed.

The string bass or double bass has virtually been replaced by the bass guitar (electric bass) in popular musical groups. While many lament the lack of the traditional double bass timbre, others have come to appreciate the clarity, range of possible timbres and speed with which the bass players can execute passages (due to the instrument's smaller scale and thinner neck).

The first electronic pickups, available for violins, flutes, clarinets, saxophones, trumpets and other acoustic instruments, required that a small hole be drilled into the body of most of these instruments, into which was fitted the pickup device (about the size of an earbud).[8] Newer models of pickups attach to the instruments themselves, using clips or adhesives. Any combination of instruments with pickups can be played into and then combined in a mixing preamplifier. The relative strength of each signal's amplitude can then be adjusted and subsequently sent on to an amplifier.

Devices which electronically alter an instrument's normal output have been developed. Some of these can divide frequencies, thereby making them sound lower by octaves from the original signal. Some devices also change the relative strengths of the harmonics present in that waveform. By so doing, the timbre as well as the range of the signal is altered. For instance, a clarinetist could produce sounds approximating a bassoon, a trumpet, a baritone horn, trombone or tuba, etc. Those devices (categorically known as "effects") can be placed in the electronic circuit after the pickup, and before the amplifier. Units are designed to be rack mounted, and have foot pedal arrangements, so that changes in timbre can be accomplished quickly by the performer.

ELECTRONIC ORGANS

In the 1950s, 60s, and well into the 70s, by far, the greatest commercial use of musical electronics was the building of electronic organs. These instruments produced electronic voltage fluctuations directly, instead of reproducing and amplifying traditional acoustic sound sources. Electronic **audio oscillators** produce periodic voltage fluctuations that are transmitted to an amplifier, and then converted to sound by a speaker system. Some manufacturers tried to design instruments that accurately reproduce the kinds of timbres and sound envelopes obtained on authentic pipe organs. None of them were very successful. Others built instruments that produced "musical" effects never found on pipe organs. Two designs were popular in the development of electronic organs.

> AUDIO OSCILLATOR: An electronic device that generates a pattern of voltage fluctuations. Four basic waveforms are commercially available; sine, sawtooth, square and triangle, yet all waveforms are theoretically possible.

---

[8] *This device, known as an electronic "pick-up," differs from a conventional microphone because vibrations to which it is sensitive are received directly from the body of the instrument. These vibrations are not first propagated through the air. Design considerations make this differentiation important.*

Magnetic Tone Generators

Possibly the oldest design for producing musical tones electronically is the magnetic tone generator (Figure 12-3). A series of metal wheels with evenly spaced "notches" were attached to a shaft that rotated them.[9] As the wheel turned near a magnet placed within a coil, the periodic changes in spacing of the rotating wheel generated voltage fluctuations within the coil. When processed by the appropriate circuitry, these produced a nearly pure sine tone. Octaves were obtained by placing many wheels on a shaft, each with 2, 4, 8, 16, 32 etc. notches on their edge. Twelve such shafts of wheels, each pre-tuned to a corresponding chromatic semitone gave a wide range of equal tempered frequencies that could be selected by pressing the appropriate key or keys. Complex timbres were obtained by coupling wheels, producing tones of the appropriate harmonic series. The amounts of each overtone were determined by a selector (timbre) switching mechanism. Certain upper overtones had to be left out, because there are no tempered tones close enough to the needed tones of the overtone series. This type of organ can still be found, although other designs have been developed.

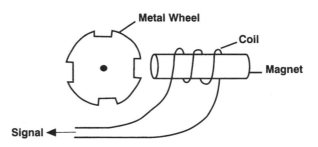

Figure 12-3. A simplified cross-section of a magnetic tone generator.

Some idea of the complexity of electronic switching mechanisms needed for electronic organs to synthesize sounds may be obtained by remembering that pipe organs have from twenty to forty stops which may be used singly or in combination, and as many as five keyboards (manuals).

Audio Oscillators

Some electronic organs make use of an electronic device called an audio oscillator.[10] This kind of electronic circuit requires alternating current or electric current which changes the direction of its flow in periodic cycles. The number of times it changes directions corresponds to the frequency that it produces. The simplest of these oscillations of periodic alternating current produces the sine waveform. The "sawtooth" waveform can also be generated.[11] This waveform

---

[9] Culver, Charles A., Musical Acoustics. (New York: McGraw-Hill Book Company, 1956), pg. 251.

[10] Jensen, David E., "Basic Principles of Electronic Sound Synthesis," doctoral dissertation, Florida State University, 1972. Also, Figures 12-4 and 12-5 are from this source.

[11] Discussed in Chapter 3 with reference to tones produced by instruments of the string family.

contains all overtones of a given fundamental frequency's overtone series. "Triangle" and "square" waveforms are also possible. These two waveforms produce all odd numbered harmonics. The physical difference between the two waveforms is that the triangle waveform produces overtones in which every other harmonic is out-of-phase. This physical difference in waveform produces an aural sensation of a timbre quite different from the timbre of the square waveforms.

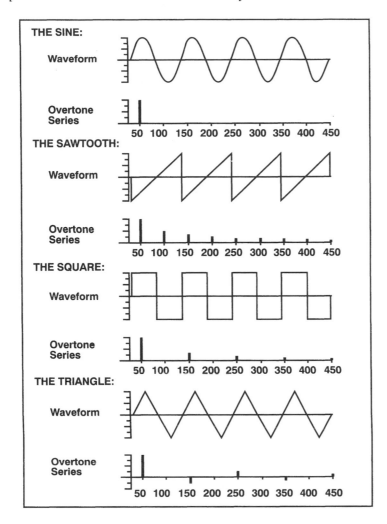

Figure 12-4. Basic Waveforms and Frequency Spectrums.

When it became possible (and feasible) to reproduce the four basic waveforms that can be formed by electronic oscillation, tones of various frequencies and timbres of diverse amplitudes, could be generated electronically. By electronic division and multiplication of frequencies, lower and higher octaves could also be produced. Electronic organs utilizing audio oscillators usually used twelve of them. Each is capable of generating one chromatic semitone of the octave. Various frequencies are selected using "tabs" connected to an elaborate switching and coupling system, and variations in timbres can be accomplished using electrical circuits known as **filters**. When a signal is passed through a filter (sometimes called a "band-pass" filter) it allows only selected frequencies to continue through a circuit. All other frequencies are rejected. By so doing, the harmonic content of a signal is changed, thus modifying the timbre of a tone.

Musical Effects

There are certain qualities inherent in electronic organs that were thought, by some, to be musical disadvantages, and by others, desirable. It was impossible, for instance, for less expensive models of electronic organs to reproduce a pipe organ's "spatial" effect; that of each tone originating from a separate pipe, and therefore, from separate locations, and of different timbres originating from combinations of pipes from different ranks. One oscillator could produce only one frequency at a time. In more expensive electronic organ models, similar spatial effects were simulated by the addition of multiple sound sources. More oscillators for each tone gave a chorus effect similar to more than one organ pipe producing the same frequency. Since organ pipes of a given frequency are rarely exactly in tune with each other (in the same way a violin section in a symphony orchestra is rarely exactly in tune at a given moment), multiple oscillators gave a similar chorus effect.[12]

Envelope circuits in electronic organs can either roughly approximate characteristics of traditional musical instruments or create different effects. Initial attack, initial decay, sustain and final decay can be varied to produce many kinds of tonal characteristics.[13] Bell-like sounds may be synthesized when a relatively long final decay is used, and the same timbre may be made to approximate a marimba's sound by using a rather rapid final decay.

In early models, to reproduce the kind of reverberation found in very large halls, a reverberation circuit was added to most electronic organs and some electronic pianos. This device transduced the electrical signal into mechanical energy and generated it through a coiled spring to delay the signal and reduce its amplitude. At the other end of the spring, the vibrations were again transduced into electrical energy. By use of multiple springs, each of different lengths, or by reintroducing the signal again at the beginning of the spring, interesting reverberation effects could be produced. Another reverberation effect called "echo" was produced by recording the signal on a magnetic tape loop and replaying it repeatedly at less and less amplitude.

Both amplitude and frequency vibrato effects were built into some electronic organs. Certain very low periodic frequency fluctuations which sound much like the vibrato of the violin tone or the human voice were obtained.

FILTER: An electronic circuit which allows only certain frequencies to pass through it while suppressing all others. Filter circuits may have controls to allow suppressed frequencies to pass at lower amplitudes.

---

[12] *The "richness" of a string section is due to a certain amount of "out-of-tuneness" at any given time. Multiple sound sources (i.e., choruses, orchestras, bands, pipe organ ranks, etc.) are often perceived as having a timbre or quality that transcends the simple multiplication of their frequencies.*

[13] *Discussed in Chapter 2, "Envelope."*

Amplitude variations were achieved by placing rotating fan blades in front of the speakers or by rotating the speakers themselves, thus utilizing the Doppler effect (Chapter 4). A certain amount of both frequency and amplitude change can be perceived by the listener when these methods are used.

Stand-alone electronic organs are today relegated to seemingly fewer and fewer applications. They may be found in houses of worship and on stage when their specific tonal characteristics are required. These instruments were often very cumbersome to transport. Attempts at miniaturization seemed to sacrifice those very tone qualities that musicians sought from them. Technological development in this area began to produce devices that offered far greater numbers of timbres. These new "**synthesizers**" provided many more varied sounds than did electronic organs, and allowed performers to alter and customize their sounds, seemingly at will.

ANALOG SYNTHESIZERS

If sounds can be changed and amplified electronically, they can also be produced without the use of traditional instruments. A new breed of instruments called "synthesizers" does just that. Synthesizers ("synths," in today's vernacular) electronically produce tones (via oscillations) through voltage fluctuations. These tones are amplified and each property of the musical tone may be "modulated" (electronically manipulated). Synth circuitry also allows for the controlled introduction of noise into the electronic pathways. Early synthesizers were boxes of electronic parts with hundreds of dials, sliders, and switches. Today, through the miracle of miniaturization, assisted by computer-produced circuit boards, synthesizers have keyboards or other controlling mechanisms whose miniaturization is limited only by what a human operator of the device can manipulate. Today, we speak of "stand-alone" synthesizers—devices used primarily for live performance; digital audio workstations—setups that often combine synthesizers and computers for the manipulation and subsequent recording of sound; and virtual synths—synthesizers that exist as software applications within computers.

There were many similarities between electronic organs, and the kind of electronic music keyboard instruments (generally termed "synthesizers") produced in the 1970s. From an historical point of view, in the here-and-now, those older synthesizers are referred to as "analog synthesizers" because their sounds were produced by fluctuating voltages in real time. One could interrupt the signal flow at any point and hear the waveform and the net effect of the electronic circuitry used to alter the waveform. Early on, one generic difference between electronic organs and analog synthesizers was that the coupling of electronic systems was originally done manually, using wires (called patch cords) on synthesizers, and was accomplished through electronic switching mechanisms on electronic organs.[14] Another difference was that synthesizers used to be modular in construction. Those modules contained three kinds of electronic circuits:

> SYNTHESIZER: A musical instrument that uses selected waveforms, modulators, and filters to alter sounds by generating and changing voltage levels.

---

[14] *This concept has come full circle. Today, digital synths offer a wide variety of predetermined sounds and timbres (called "patches") to choose from.*

1) electronic sound sources, including audio oscillators and noise generators, 2) signal modifiers, consisting of amplifiers, balanced modulators, filters, and reverberation modules, and 3) auxiliary controls including envelope generators, touch controlled voltage generators, sequencers, and possibly other modules. Electronic organs, on the other hand, had the parameters of frequency, amplitude, timbre and envelope predetermined, and each was selected by a series of switches. Even these differences finally gave way. Electronic organs actually evolved into analog synthesizers.

Electronic Sound Sources

As previously discussed, audio oscillators can produce one or more of the four basic waveforms (sine, sawtooth, square or triangle). Analog synthesizer oscillator modules have controls for varying the frequencies of their output signal. Some contained a "coarse" tuning frequency selector and a "fine" tuning frequency selector. By combining or subtracting the outputs of two or more oscillators, tones having various combinations of the basic waveforms were possible.

Noise generators were also a part of most synthesizers. As discussed in Part I of this book, noise plays an important role in music. The output of the white noise generator is a random sampling of all audible frequencies at equal amplitudes (Chapter 2). The psychoacoustic effect of such white noise is that it is perceived to contain a predominance of high frequencies. Remember, the hearing apparatus does not respond to all frequencies at equal loudness (See Figure 6-1). This effect prompted the development of what has been termed a **pink noise** generator. Pink noise is actually white noise that has been filtered so most all the frequencies of the audible spectrum can be perceived at nearly equal loudness.

Signal Modifiers

Amplifiers were included on analog synthesizers to offer gain (amplitude) control for the signal passed through them. Without an amplifier for each oscillator in the circuit, any composite signal would be increased only by the amplification factor for which each module was designed. The final processed signal could contain far too much or too little amplitude. For this reason separate gain controls for each oscillator were important.

Balanced modulators accepted two or more incoming signals and produced the sums and differences of the input frequencies as an output. The original input frequencies were then suppressed. The resulting tones were not necessarily a part of the natural harmonic series, but rather, founded upon the sums and differences of the input frequencies. For instance, if frequencies of 300 Hz and 400 Hz were fed as inputs to the balanced modulator, their sum (700 Hz), and their difference (100 Hz), would be the output. Output from balanced modulators is called **ring modulation**. Ring modulation has little basis in our traditional harmonic system; therefore, its musical effect is quite unusual and has been often used to create or accentuate the "electronic" sound of music.

PINK NOISE: Pink noise is white noise that has been filtered to allow all frequencies of the audible spectrum to be perceived at equal loudness. All manner of noise generators are available commercially. Many are named for colors.

BALANCED MODULATOR: A balanced modulator is basically a carrier signal with side bands (information encoded in the carrier signal). The carrier signal is reversed in phase, resulting in cancellation, so only the side bands remain.

RING MODULATION: Frequencies obtained by sum and difference tones of two input signals. The input frequencies are usually suppressed so the output contains only the resultant sum and difference tones.

Filters, as discussed in the section on electronic organs, allow only certain frequency ranges contained in a signal to pass. Other frequencies are suppressed. Filter modules allow the selection of either a cutoff frequency above or below those frequencies that will be suppressed, or a bandwidth through which frequencies may pass or be rejected. Filters that suppress frequencies above a selected frequency are called **low pass filters**. They allow low frequencies to pass in the circuit. Filters that suppress frequencies below a selected frequency are **high pass filters. Bandpass filters** accept (pass on) frequencies only within a particular range. Thus, either the fundamental frequency or any portion of the overtone series may be suppressed or passed on to the output of a filter module. Filters used in various overlapping configurations are termed "cascades." A series of bandpass filters with amplitude adjustments covering the entire audio spectrum may be thought of as a **graphic equalizer**.[15]

As used by electronic organs, reverberation modules made use of a mechanical delay caused by transducing an electrical signal into mechanical energy. The resultant vibrations were sent through a coiled spring and thus delayed and reduced in amplitude by their transmission through the spring. The vibrations were again converted to electrical energy where the signal was reintroduced again at the beginning of the spring. This process continued until all acoustic energy had been dissipated. On these modules, the reverberation delay, time, and the rate of decay could be controlled manually.

Auxiliary Controls

The function of the group modules referred to as auxiliary controls was to provide other output signals or to operate switching systems for controlling the main signal from the oscillators.

The envelope generator is a voltage control module which uses an electronic signal to control the four temporal parameters of a tone (attack, initial decay, sustain, and release). By use of these electronic controls, envelopes can be created that can occur much faster than human dexterity allows, were these controls operated manually (see Figure 12-5). The amplitude of the input signal can be shaped by the control voltage produced by the envelope generator.

Another common auxiliary control is the low frequency oscillator (**LFO**). This control produces a periodic waveform, most often below the level of human perception. Although we can't hear the LFO as a musical tone, we perceive its effect upon tones within the range of human hearing, in the forms of periodic modulation of pitch, loudness, and timbre.

---

[15] *Graphic equalizers are typically found in sound systems as a part of the pre-amplifier.*

LOW PASS FILTER: Filters that suppress frequencies above a preset frequency cutoff point but allow all frequencies below the cutoff point to pass.

HIGH PASS FILTER: Filters that suppress frequencies below a preset frequency cutoff point but allow all frequencies above the cutoff point to pass.

BANDPASS FILTER: Filters that are sensitive to a particular range of audio frequencies and pass them through while rejecting all frequencies outside that audio "band."

GRAPHIC EQUALIZER: A signal processor that allows the amplitudes of specific frequencies (and to a lesser degree their neighboring frequencies) to be increased or decreased.

LOW FREQUENCY OSCILLATOR (LFO): A specialized oscillator, usually outputting a waveform whose frequency is well below the audible limits of human hearing. LFO's applied to other oscillators produce periodic variations in pitch. When applied to amplifiers, periodic variations in loudness are produced.

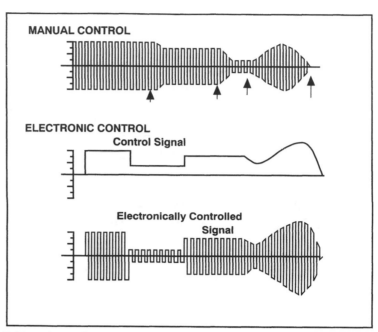

Figure 12-5. Envelope Control—Manual and Electronic.

A touch-controlled voltage generator was included to **trigger** the signal instead of producing the signal by increasing the gain on the amplifier. Manual opening and closing of the gain control would simply not give a musical attack. The trigger mechanism was a keyboard, a metallic ribbon, or a series of push buttons. Each, when depressed, completed an electronic circuit that allowed the signal to travel on. By using such a triggering system, analog synthesizers could be made to produce tones of pre-selected frequencies, timbres, amplitudes, and envelopes by connecting the proper circuit and then triggering them.

In analog synthesizers, a **sequencer** is a time controlled triggering mechanism. Instead of manually depressing a trigger, this type of sequencer can be programmed to automatically trigger a signal (most often a series of musical tones) at pre-selected time intervals. By setting the sequencer to trigger (for instance) six times per second, and by coupling it with the manual touch controlled voltage generator (trigger), tones can be produced having a tremolo-like sound. More complicated aural displays can be programmed and actuated by a sequencing circuit. In more modern, advanced digital synthesizers, the term "sequencer" has developed into quite a different meaning. Today, we interchange the terms "sample," "loop," and "sequence." These terms refer to the ability of a music producing machine to select, play, and replay musical material.

DIGITAL SYNTHESIZERS

Today, using digital technology, the synth, can be thought of as an extension of a computer. Let's first look at what the computer is, then we can better understand this new breed of instrument and how it works, and how it interfaces with other machines that use digital means to communicate.

TRIGGER: A switch which completes an electronic circuit. The term "trigger" is used in place of the term "keyboard" on synthesizers because, even though the mechanism looks like a keyboard, often it is preset to trigger tones which are not of the equal temperament system.

SEQUENCER: (Old) A triggering mechanism that could be set to alternately open and close a circuit at timed intervals; and (new), a device that records triggering information by storing and replaying key-press information.

170

The Computer

Actually, a computer is a modular device whose central "brain" is a **CPU**. The CPU translates and directs information stored in it or fed to it by some input device. Everything else can be thought of as a module or add-on. There is a hard drive or other mass-storage computer memory device; a disk drive and/or a CD/DVD drive that stores, sorts and/or retrieves data; and there are peripherals to input data including a keyboard, a joystick, a mouse, a touch screen, a pen, or other control surface. And, there are output display devices including a **CRT**, a **plasma monitor**, or an **LCD**, and also a modem, possibly a speaker or two, and a printer. All of these devices are referred to generically as "hardware." "Software" comes in two forms. One configures the system and makes it run; sort of a map by which the computer knows where and how to store information. This is commonly called its "operating system." The other kind is called "applications software." It is these programs that turn the CPU into a word processor, a graphic arts display, a music maker, or any number of other ways in which computers can work for us.

If it is music that we want, there are software packages that will instruct our computer to be a music writing and printing device, or a music making and storing device. In fact, we can connect our computer to a synth and as a kind of dedicated computer itself, there are a number of very musical things that can happen.

Synths

Because of an agreement by electronic music instrument manufacturers and the computer industry, all electronic music instruments can communicate with each other via a digital coding and formatting system called **MIDI**. The other part of that agreement is that all plugs and cables that connect these MIDI devices together will all use the same configuration. MIDI technology was standardized in 1983 and, although it has undergone some revision, it is the protocol that helps to provide us with ringtones, printed music, audio for video games, and audio/video synchronization, today.

Synths also have a CPU as their brain. It is the task of the synthesizer's CPU to translate and route digital information initiated by a **controller** to modules that are sound producing or sound modifying circuits. A controller can be located on board, it can be a stand-alone device, or, for that matter, it can be computer-based software. These controllers take many forms. Probably the best known and most easily recognized is the piano keyboard. Here, however, there is no lever action that either strikes or plucks a string, or the opening of a set of pipes to a wind chest; nor is there a gate that sends alternating voltages to an amplifying circuit. This synth keyboard is a triggering mechanism that sends binary information to the CPU concerning how hard the key was struck, how long it stayed depressed, and which key was struck. It can be electronically connected to any sound producing module. It's not hard to imagine that we could select the timbre characteristics of any number of kinds of piano brands, organs, harpsichords, claviers of all types; or we might wish to trigger a sampled voice saying "INTRODUCTORY MUSICAL ACOUSTICS," a sampled set of gamelan chimes, car horns, dogs barking, or a full symphony orchestra! All are equally possible using a controller.

CPU: Central Processing Unit. The brain of any computer.

CRT: Cathode Ray Tube. This device can be a television, a PC monitor, or an oscilloscope. A beam of electrons is rapidly painted horizontally across a phosphorescent screen tracing images as it does so.

PLASMA MONITOR: A device that produces video images by creating gas discharges. These discharges cause ultra-violet rays to excite combinations of red, green, and blue phosphorus, which in turn create the images we view.

LCD: A thin, flat panel used for electronically displaying information such as text, images, and moving pictures. It is an electronically-modulated optical device made up of any number of pixels filled with quartz liquid crystals and arrayed in front of a light source (backlight) or reflector to produce images.

MIDI: "Musical Instrument Digital Interface" A set of internationally agreed upon specifications for the digital coding of communication between electronic musical instruments.

CONTROLLER: A triggering mechanism that sends MIDI data whose values can be varied in real time.

Controllers are also made so that those of us who are not fully functional as keyboardists can also get into the fun of electronic music making. Electronic drums and even full drum set configurations can be used as controllers. There is an electronic woodwind instrument that configures as either a recorder, or as a Boehm system woodwind (flute or saxophone). Stick strokes are used as triggers in drum machines and a player's wind and tongue serve as the controllers for electronic woodwinds.[16] Even foot pedal controllers are available. Attempts to configure brass controllers have also been made.

An integral part of a digital synth is a **sequencer**. These too, may be on board, stand alone or computer-based software. Sequencers store and play back key-press information that includes the attack, amplitude, duration, and envelope. Specific key-press information is transmitted on one or more of sixteen MIDI channels to selected tone producing modules, each with a unique, user controlled, MIDI channel number.

Particular sounds[17] are stored in the onboard computer memory of most synths. The number of sounds is determined by the size of the computer's memory. Most synths have a minimum of 128, and usually many more sounds are available; all of which may be combined or altered to make yet even other timbres. These are stored in the synth in **ROM** chips. Even more sounds are available via other storage media and online at various websites. Sources of these sounds may be **sampled sounds**, simple waves, or manufactured complex waveforms. No matter what the source, these sounds, in the form of serial binary digits, must be sent on to the D/A (digital to analog) converter, then to a preamp/amp circuit for traditional analog audio processing, converting the signal to audible sound.

SEQUENCER: Sequencers manage control information (such as control voltage or note on/off commands) to be sent to electronic musical instruments to produce audio output. Most modern sequencers now feature audio editing and processing capabilities as well. Consequently, the terms "music sequencer" and "digital audio workstation" are often used interchangeably.

ROM: "Read Only Memory." ROM information is a part of a microchip and cannot be changed; only accessed. A compact disc's information is ROM.

SAMPLED SOUNDS: Digitally encoded analog sounds. Generally acoustic instrument's sounds throughout its range are sampled at thousands of times per second and stored as "samples" to be digitally "read into" a synth.

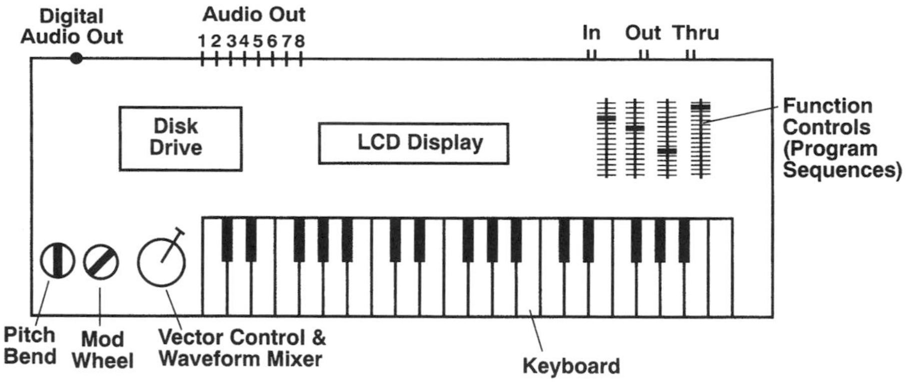

Figure 12- 6. A typical digital synth configuration

[16] *MIDI AMERICA, Inc,* The Musical PC, *Geary Yelton, editor; Appendix D, "MIDI 1.0 Specification Tables," 1992, pp. 337- 346.*
This book is an easily accessible compendium of how to use your computer and synth together. Even its appendix is easily readable. It is the sort of book that novices find "friendly."

[17] *Sometimes called "patches." A hangover from the days when patch cords were strung from oscillator to oscillator and then on to amplifying circuits.*

Other common synth features include specialized ports for the transmission and reception of data. MIDI ports are found on the backs of keyboard units, and in the boxes that accompany wind and percussion controllers. There are three kinds of ports: IN, OUT, and THRU. The "in" port receives all MIDI information (in 8 bit bytes). This information concerns which notes to play, when to play them, how long to play them, what modulation should occur while they are played, and on what channel to play them. The "out" port is capable of sending anything already in the memory of a particular module, and also sends to other units, information that a performer plays into the synth in real time. Signals coming from the "thru" port are duplicates of information from the "in" port, and in this manner they may be distributed to other MIDI devices. In addition to jacks for devices such as sustain pedals and channel switches, the backs of synths also have standard stereo L & R analog outputs, and perhaps other analog output jacks for separate channel distribution, so that each unique timbre may have its own output. Newer models may also have an assortment of digital inputs and outputs such as **USB, Firewire, Lightpipe**, and even wireless sends and receives.

Almost all modern synths and modules have LCD displays that ease communication between the synth and its human operator. The LCD display shows the status of selected patches and patch edits. Many synths have ports for external memory devices. The newest synths are called "workstations." These function as music production appliances and allow many sounds to be edited, sampled, sequenced and stored. They really are a "band in a box" because many of their sounds are digital recordings of acoustic musical instruments.

Home Theater

Another area that has developed since the end of the twentieth century is the inevitable marriage of one's listening system to the television and to video playback and gaming as well. While there was a time in the early 70s when "quadraphonic" sound was explored, it did not really catch on during our "vinyl years." The new fashion with home theater owners is to create a "holographic" sound in which the listener feels as if they are within the space visualized on the screen.

There came a desire to create more lifelike and engaging entertainment experiences. In order to enhance a sense of "being in the action," systems such as "5.1 sound" were developed. These systems were an outgrowth of the older experiments with quadraphonic or surround sound, which placed main stereo speakers in front of the listener and smaller satellite speakers behind. Sometimes there were real attempts at creating true four-channel sound, but more often, a microprocessor simply filtered and delayed the delivery of the stereo signal to the rear speakers, simulating the sensation of room ambience, placing the listener in the middle of the sound, rather than in front of it.

Because of the expense and cumbersome nature of multi-track recording tape, and the improbability of stereo phonographs accurately reproducing anything more than a stereo signal, early surround sound fell by the wayside. When methods for

USB: Universal Serial Bus. A data transfer system provided to interconnect multiple computer-based devices.

FIREWIRE: The brand name of a particular kind of digital data transfer protocol.

LIGHTPIPE: A transmitting media used to interconnect and transfer data via pulses of light through fiber optic strands.

digitizing, compressing and storing both video and audio signals were developed, true surround sound became feasible. The new optical disc digital technologies allowed many discrete audio channels to be recorded and stored on inexpensive discs that also may contain video signals. Those signals are read by computer-enhanced amplifiers so that true surround sound is accurate and economically feasible.

The most common type of 5.1 surround sound uses six audio channels, each carrying an audio signal that is independent from the others. Two speakers are placed in front and to the left and right of the listener. Also, a center channel is place directly in front. A second set of speakers is placed to the left and right, behind the listener. A sixth speaker (the .1), is called a sub-woofer, or LFO (low frequencey oscillator), and carries only very low bass signals (i.e., the rumble of street traffic, the foot steps of a dinosaur, etc.). It's placed towards the front of the listening field. This array of speakers creates a listening experience that recreates advanced theater systems, and perhaps, the real world. Other systems, such as 6.1 and 7.1 simply add speakers to the sides and rear center of the listening field. Some systems now try to recreate the sensation of height within the sound field.

Still other 5.1 systems use what is called a matrix to deliver signals to speakers and create the desired surround sound effect. In a matrix system, signals from several channels are combined and delivered to specialized amplifiers that then separate and send the audio signals to the correct speakers (and the video to the screen). Whether using a discrete, matrix, or other system for creating surround sound, today's home theater technologies truly rival what was only once available in the finest theaters and theme parks.

Video and computer screens are now being changed from a 4:3 aspect ratio to a 16:9 ratio to more closely approximate the aspect ratio of Hollywood movies. Many movies that are actually filmed in widescreen are reduced for showing at a 4:3 ratio on older TV sets by using a technique called "pan and scan." A 4:3 section of the entire screen is selected leaving the sides of the 16 x 9 ratio picture out entirely. Some new cell phones convert the picture ratio from 4:3 to 16:9 just by turning the phone from a vertical to a horizontal plane.

OUR FUTURE—MUSICAL SCIENCE FICTION?

With the advent of hand-held audio devices, MP3 and other compression technologies, the compacting of the personal computer into the cell phone, our present musical lives are complete with excellent holographic sound fidelity and "take-it-with-you-and-throw-it-away" music. What else could we ask for? Remember the "cute" lyrics from Rogers and Hammerstein's musical *Oklahoma*? "Everything's up-to-date in Kansas City. They've gone about as far as they can go!"[18] It's a clever line because we know that technology continues to refine and develop.

---

[18] Oklahoma *was the first Broadway musical to have an original cast recording released. The year was 1943. Historical perspective is important — even when looking at technology. We can see if and where we are going only by looking at where we have been.*

There will certainly be more "Gee Whiz" in our future. Computers with three window screens, soft, roll-up screens, panoramic screens, and more innovations are on the horizon and already in development. High definition video is here and possibilities for many tracks exist on the Blu-Ray definition video discs. It is possible to place 5.1, 6.1, 6.2 or even 7.1& 2 sound tracks on a single disc. While current optical disc technologies such as DVD, DVD±R, DVD±RW, and DVD-RAM rely on a red laser to read and write data, the new format uses a blue-violet laser instead, hence the name Blu-ray. Despite the different type of lasers used, Blu-ray products can easily be made backwards compatible with CDs and DVDs through the use of a BD/DVD/CD compatible optical pickup unit. The benefit of using a blue-violet laser (405nm) is that it has a shorter wavelength than a red laser (650nm), which makes it possible to focus the laser spot with even greater precision. This allows data to be packed more tightly and stored in less space, so it's possible to fit more data on the disc even though it's the same size as a CD/DVD. This, together with the change of numerical aperture to 0.85, is what enables Blu-ray discs to hold 25GB/50GB. Recent developments in the industry have pushed the storage capacity to 500GB on a single disc by placing digital bits and bytes vertically on the disc in up to 20 layers.

The physical laws of sound and audio have not changed; but recording, storing and reproduction systems are still being developed. Learning to play an instrument and getting immediate feedback is already in place as a possibility on the internet. Downloading accompaniments that follow the performer are available. Peer-to-peer technology allows music lessons to take place over vast distances with many of the world's most accomplished players and teachers. There is even an Internet II that is dedicated to communication between universities and their faculties. On this second, closed-system internet, bandwidth is 100 times broader and delays are now so small as to be infinitesimal. Although, it is interesting to note that even at this level, the playing of duets or ensembles between remote locations is not satisfying. The real-time delay (1/100th of a second) is still too great for a satisfying musical experience.

What determines the success of the next great innovation? Excellent ideas abound, but often do not become part of the mainstream for decades and in some extreme cases, for a century or more. For instance, the tools for the synthesis of sounds were available to us in the 19th century, but were not economically feasible to manufacture at that time. Nor had a purpose been thought of for them. In today's world, innovation is often tempered by "glitches" in new technologies, litigation regarding the ownership of the intellectual property rights of those technologies, consumer unfamiliarity with the new technologies, and a reluctance on the part of manufacturers to provide capital for the refinement of the new technologies.

We live in the midst of this technological revolution. It would be an "evolution," if changes in our machines of music did not happen so fast. We are already connecting our music machines, our video machines and our telephones to our computers. We are well into the age of "digits and widgits," and this book, as time progresses, may be out of date soon, only to re-emerge as perhaps a pod-cast, or exclusively in the digital realm.

DISCUSSION QUESTIONS FOR CHAPTER TWELVE

1. How may a flute's sound be electronically amplified? A violin's sound?

2. It is possible to electronically make a trumpet sound three octaves lower than the note it produces. How?

3. What advantages can you see for electronic pianos? What disadvantages?

4. Discuss differences in the sounds produced by pipe organs and electronic organs.

5. How do electronic organs differ from synthesizers?

6. How do analog synthesizers differ from digital synths?

7. How might a cymbal crash be approximated on a synthesizer; the sound of waves at the seashore; a siren; a violin; a string quartet?

8. If a sequencer were programmed to trigger 30 attacks per second, what audible effect would be produced?

Index